1993

BOTANY for GARDENERS

HAROLD WILLIAM RICKETT
THE NEW YORK BOTANICAL GARDEN

THE MACMILLAN COMPANY
NEW YORK

To

EZRA JACOB KRAUS
(remembering certain early efforts to teach botany)
I gratefully dedicate this book

Preface

This book grew out of a course of lectures given at The New York Botanical Garden during the past several years to a mixed audience of gardeners, nurserymen, teachers, housewives, professional men, and others. Such courses have long been given by various members of the staff of the Garden; it was my erstwhile colleague Dr. Wendell Holmes Camp who suggested to me that we put our elementary course into a book. Other places, other duties claimed him, and I realized that if this were ever to be done I should have to do it alone. I regret this, for it would have been a better book had Camp had a hand in it.

I have attempted, then, a presentation of the basic facts and principles of botany for those who have had no previous schooling in science. But one cannot write on any science without being at least a little technical. Though the professional botanist may consider my account too simple to be of any real use, the layman may find it tougher going than—let us say—the admirable stories of Agatha Christie. There is a limit to simplification, if one is going to tell the truth. However, I have been at some pains to spare the reader the usual horrific array of botanical terms and names which the botanist considers essential to the making of a book.

Botany has become so vast, so diversified, so specialized, that it is perhaps impossible for one person to treat it even in this elementary fashion without making mistakes. I can only hope that my errors are few and unimportant.

Most of the drawings were made from living plants; some from microscopic sections of parts of plants. A few—easily identified by any botanist—are diagrams based on the work of others. I hope that they will encourage the reader to look about him, in his garden and elsewhere, with and without magnifying lenses.

H. W. R.

January 1957

Contents

CONTENTS

Prologue

WHAT IS BOTANY?

This is not a book on *how to grow plants;* it is rather on *how plants grow.* Botany is often confused with horticulture, and the botanist is often expected to be able to answer questions about the kinds of plants in the garden and their culture; but botany* deals with all plants, wild as well as cultivated, with their food, their functions, their inner structure, their growth, their reproduction, their evolution and breeding, their diseases, and so on. Botany is the running-mate of zoology, the study of animals; botany and zoology together make up biology, the study of life (of course, from the scientific point of view).

All this may sound as if the scientific study of plants has nothing to do with growing them. There are still those (they used to be more numerous) who like to think so, who pride themselves on the "purity" of their science, and who are perhaps somewhat contemptuous of its applications. But the fact is that knowledge is apt to be useful, whether the scientist likes it or not. Our cultural practices grew up in remote antiquity through long processes of trial and error; the most successful methods were adopted, long before any one knew what made them successful. But in modern times our ways of growing plants have been enormously expanded and clarified by the development of natural science. In controlling plant diseases the gardener and farmer use knowledge that comes from the laboratories where botanists (neither gardeners nor farmers) study molds and other fungi, elucidating their nutrition, their life cycles, their structure and breeding. Our success in producing kinds of plants more resistant to disease or with more attrac-

---

* To be sure, the word is derived from a Greek word meaning "good to eat"; the earliest students of plants had such practical matters very much in mind, but the word has lost its old sense, and is now applied to the pure science.

3

tive flowers rests largely upon experiments performed in the garden of a Bohemian monastery by one of the brothers who had been schooled in natural science. Our vast science of bacteriology, with all that it means to our health, is based on the researches of amateur scientists who acquired magnifying lenses of improved design and workmanship and who were curious about the minute things visible through them—with no suspicion of their importance to their descendants.

Botany is not horticulture; still less is it agriculture; but it provides the background of knowledge for those arts just as physics makes it possible to manufacture radios and chemistry is necessary to our supply of vitamins.

WHAT IS A PLANT?

Our business is with plants, their forms and functions. But what is a plant? How can we define or even describe a plant? The elm or maple or oak outside the window is a plant. How describe this strong thing that stands there over so many years, its feet in the earth, its myriad leaves spread to heaven? It bears flowers also, and fruit in its season. Within its seemingly inert trunk is living protoplasm, the substance of all life, which consumes food as your own flesh does. The grass around its base also is a plant. Its creeping stems send up their narrow blades and feathered culms. Its roots, like those of the tree, penetrate the hidden recesses of the earth. The moss at the base of the trunk and the green smear that adorns the shady side of its bark—these also are plants. So is the cluster of toadstools nearby, which mark the site of a tree taken out years ago.

So in a few square yards of earth we can find many different kinds of plants. For the gardener plants are chiefly his trees and his grass, his roses and his lilies and his daffodils and his larkspur and phlox and zinnias and asters, his beans and peas and lettuce and cabbage and tomatoes and corn. For the farmer they are above all his wheat and oats and barley and corn, his pasture grasses and clover and alfalfa, his soybeans and peanuts and cotton, his potatoes and turnips, his grapevines and apples and cherries. How can we describe or explain all this host of diverse forms? What is common to them all? Where shall we begin? With their leaves, which make their food (and ours) within their minute cells? With their stems and branches, through whose veins sap rises and food moves, and from whose tips new leaves and flowers bud out? With their flowers, fruit, and seed, in infinite variety, which adorn our gardens and load our tables with succulence and delight? Where shall we begin?

WHERE DO PLANTS COME FROM?

Where did they come from, all these plants? They were not always there. The garden was made, planted; the farmland was cleared. Seed was put in the earth; or young plants were purchased and carefully installed—and these must have come from seed somewhere in their ancestry. In fact all the plants of your garden came from seed if you trace them back far enough; all the saplings and shrubs and cuttings and small plants of every description which have gone to make the garden or the farm (all, that is, save perhaps a few ferns, and such mosses and toadstools and other small weeds that have crept in of their own accord).

Of course many kinds of plants are not grown from seed today; for example the ordinary potato, and most of our garden geraniums. But these cultivated races came from wild ancestors, which once reproduced their kind by seed as wild plants do today.

Perhaps it would be a good idea to begin this book with seeds, as you begin your garden. Many botanical textbooks begin with seeds; with beans, in fact. The devotion of botanical writers to beans has occasioned much playful and even derisive comment— perhaps ever since old Nehemiah Grew started the fashion in 1684.

But where does the seed come from? Tomato seed comes from a tomato, which in turn comes from a small white and yellow flower. Beans and peas come from pods, which were also the product of flowers. Seed of columbine, larkspur, nasturtium, hollyhock, poppies come from various small containers, capsules and the like, formed by flowers and growing to maturity after the fall of the petals. Seed of orchids, as fine as dust, germinated with infinite patience and skill in glass vessels, comes from a capsule formed beneath the petals. Even grains of corn* and wheat come from flowers, small flowers collected in the ears of these cereals.

Small wonder that flowers have always been of special interest to man: they were the symbol of fertility, of the renewal of life, even before they served his aesthetic purposes. Ancient man offered the fruits of the earth to his ancestors and to his gods. Paintings on Egyptian walls thousands of years old show processions of priests and priestesses carrying flowers to their god. Flowers are named in the poems and proverbs of the children of Israel. Flowers were laid on Roman altars and garlanded the godlike Caesars. Flowers symbolized the sufferings of Christian martyrs and the virtues which they practiced.

Throughout human history flowers have furnished designs for artists and craftsmen; today they look out from our draperies, our wallpapers, our dishes; they decorate our gardens and parks, and our homes. Flowers comfort the sick-room; they welcome a new arrival into the world and are the last tribute to one who has departed.

But—when all this has been said—*in the life of the plant* (rather than in our lives) flowers are important chiefly as organs of reproduction. They form fruit and seeds—a new generation. They perpetuate the species. It is true that not all plants form flowers: there are also mushrooms and seaweeds and mosses and ferns. But the flowering plants are half of all the plants there are on earth; and in their importance and interest for us they far outweigh the other half. It is true also that many flowering plants can reproduce without flowering—by tubers, bulbs, runners, and the like. But the dissemination of the flowering plants over the earth and their evolution into all the varied forms which we see today have occurred largely through flowering—through the production of fruit and seed.

---

* In Britain "corn" includes all the cereal grains—wheat, oats, barley, and the rest; and refers especially to the first of these. Maize was first called "Indian corn"; and to all of us on this side of the Atlantic has become simply "corn."

1

⫷⫷⫷⫷⫷

The Seed We Plant

WHAT'S IN A SEED?

On a day in spring we stretch a string across our garden,
open a shallow trench in the soil, and drop into it a row of seeds.
We close the trench and smooth down the soil over the buried
seeds. Then we wait. A few days later the surface is pierced by
small green things struggling up from below. Our seeds have
germinated; the new year is on the way.

The form taken by the new plants depends, of course, on what
we planted. If we planted corn grains we expect to see the narrow
pointed green spikes of corn seedlings; if we placed beans in the
trench, a sort of hoop or crook first appears above ground, soon
straightening and bearing on its upper end a pair of small, thick
and somewhat wrinkled objects. Our feelings on this point are
emphatic. If we planted radish seeds we should be shocked to
see pea vines emerging; we are confident that seeds of a certain
size, form, color, hardness, and so forth will give a particular kind
of crop, according to the label on the packet.

But it is not the external features of the seed that determine the
kind of plant that grows from it. The seed-coat does not form any
part of the plant that emerges; this comes from within. You actually
place in the soil small plants of corn or bean, radish or pea; small
plants already formed, wrapped in a more or less hard and impervious envelope. If a dormant seed is dissected, the parts of
this plantlet may be seen.

Most seeds are inconveniently small for dissection. A petunia

7

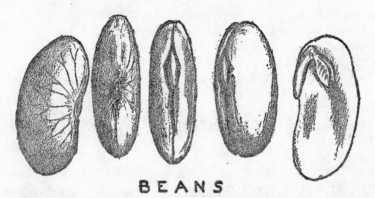

BEANS

seed is about one-fiftieth of an inch across; other kinds are even smaller. Orchid seed is dustlike; one capsule has been estimated to contain two million. For dissection it is best to choose something larger; which is doubtless why so many textbooks, as already noticed, begin with beans. It would be troublesome to use a seed so small that it could not be seen (to paraphrase the old man a-sitting on a gate). To go to the other extreme, and use the largest seed known, would be equally inconvenient, for obvious reasons; perhaps the largest seed is that of a coconut. Beans, then, it shall be.

A bean, as it comes from the packet, is hard and dry; it is difficult to credit it with life, to believe that it has any activity akin to our own. Even to cut it apart and see its parts is difficult. If, however, one soaks it in water for a few hours, it becomes much softer; and an outer layer, now changed into a delicate and fragile membrane, slips off easily. This is the seed-coat.

When the coat has been removed, two rounded objects are visible which fill almost all of the space within; the two "halves" familiar not only in beans but also in peas and peanuts and sunflower seed and found (with careful study) even in such odd seeds as those inside walnuts. These two things are called, in botanical jargon, cotyledons*: they are considered, in spite of their appear-

---

* Derived from a Greek word which was first applied to something quite different; it means literally a "cup-shaped hollow"; the present meaning is therefore purely arbitrary.

ance, to be leaves, the first leaves of the new plant. If they are carefully separated, it will be seen that they are both attached, at nearly the same point, to a small tapering narrow body that lies along their edges (near the scar on the seed-coat). Since leaves commonly grow attached to a stem (or to a branch, which is the same thing), we refer to this minute object as the primary stem of the plant. At its other end, however—the end farthest from the place where the cotyledons are attached—is the rounded tip from which the first root will grow. The inner structure of this stem is not wholly like that of the stems and branches that will appear later; it is not a true stem, but transitional in nature. For the purposes of this book, however, it may be referred to as the primary stem of the embryo.

Lift one cotyledon completely off, breaking the connection between it and the primary stem; growing from the extreme tip of the latter, but curved so as to project into the narrow space between the two cotyledons—the space enclosed by their almost flat inner surfaces—is a small tuft of minute leaves. This is the first bud of the plant; exactly what is in a bud, and what comes from it, will become clearer as the germination of the seed is described, and is further elucidated in a later place (p. 39). Even in this its dormant state it is easy to see that its leaves are truly leaflike in appearance, much more so than the cotyledons. They are flat, pointed, veined.*

These are all the parts that you will find in a bean, within the seed-coat: cotyledons and a bud, all attached to a stem, at the other end of which is a root-tip. They are all joined, all form one body, one embryo—a complete plant with the beginnings of stem,

---

* The parts of the embryo have received several more or less fanciful names, to be found in textbooks. The primary stem with its root-tip is generally called the hypocotyl; which means "under the cotyledons," as it is after germination. Another term is caulicle (cauliculus in Latin, a "small stem"); but this has been variously applied and may be confusing. The root-tip is sometimes called the radicle (radiculus, a "small root"); but this word has been applied to the whole hypocotyl, and may also be confusing. The first bud receives the name epicotyl; which means "upon the cotyledons," for after germination it stands upon or above the point of attachment of the two primary leaves. From its appearance it has also been fancifully named the plumule; Nehemiah Grew in 1684 named it simply the plume. (Plumula in Latin means a "small feather.")

leaves, and root. This embryo is what you plant, wrapped up in its protective coat; this is what pushes its way up into the air and light.

HOW THE SEED GERMINATES

That little hoop or crook already noticed as the first part to appear is the stem. The root-tip, at its end, has by now sent a root down into the earth; a root which branches, forming other roots, and appropriating a small sphere of soil for its use. The other end of the stem is at first held by the two fat cotyledons to which it is attached, these still enclosed by the seed-coat. The stem is more or less firmly fastened at both ends; accordingly, as it lengthens, it bends, it arches; it backs out of the seed-coat, as it were. The force of its growth is considerable; it is soon sufficient to drag the cotyledons up through the soil, perhaps with part of the seed-coat still adhering to them. The stem now stands erect,

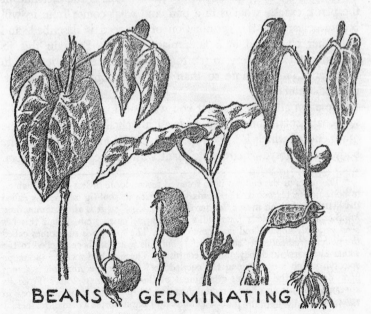

BEANS GERMINATING

and displays its primary leaves, the cotyledons, somewhat shrunken, as may be seen; which spread apart and do their best to look and act like leaves. The bud between them is now revealed, and rapidly enlarges; its two leaves assume a more bean-leaflike shape, and are carried up on a length of new stem*; and between *their* stalks it may be seen that more leaves, more stem are in the making. Our young plant is no longer pallid, dormant, embryonic, coiled and cramped within a hard shell; it is green, erect, an actively growing, creative organism, with an outward form familiar to those who grow beans.

This history is characteristic of a multitude of seeds of many kinds of plants. In spite of vast differences among them in size, shape, color, hardness, they contain embryos consisting of a stem which bears at one end two leaves enfolding a minute bud (or the rudiment of one) and at the other end the beginning of a root. Seeds of some other plants, however, do not germinate in this way. A pea, though closely related to a bean and having the same parts, does not send its cotyledons above the ground. The primary stem does not lengthen, does not lift its first leaves; its nether end puts out a root, and the bud which lies between the cotyledons grows up and emerges from the soil. The first leaves which you see as a result of planting peas and some kinds of beans are *not* the first leaves of the embryo; *they* are still beneath the surface.

Those swollen leaves, the cotyledons, are reservoirs of food; carbohydrates (starch, sugars, and the like), protein, fat. We ourselves use them as food; when we plant beans or peas our ultimate aim is to obtain a new supply of cotyledons. As root and bud enlarge and add new roots, new leaves, new lengths of stem, the food which they use in their growth is withdrawn from the cotyledons, which consequently become flaccid and shrunken. Their elevation into the air is not necessary to their usefulness. But when they *are* carried up, they become green and to some extent supplement the nourishment of the embryo by manufacturing new food from the simple substances of air and water, as leaves usually do (pp. 77, 78).

---

* Even these leaves, it will be noticed, are not like those that come later; they are not divided into threes.

THE VARIETY IN SEEDS

In one way a bean is not typical of seeds. Many seeds have one more part. The embryo of a magnolia seed, for instance, does not fill the space within the seed-coat. Most of the bulk of the seed is occupied by a rather oily material, in which the minute embryo lies embedded. This material is the endosperm*; in different kinds of seeds it may be hard or soft, floury or oily or waxy or horny. Usually when endosperm is abundant the embryo is very small, its stem very short, its bud nothing but a minute tip, its cotyledons thin, often folded together. The seed of the castor-oil plant is like this. One must split open the horny endosperm (and it is necessary first to soften it by soaking it in water); the two thin, leaflike cotyledons lie pressed together in a cleft within it; they are joined at their bases to a short nubbin of a stem. A buckwheat grain is much the same. If one cuts across this triangular grain, one may see the two cotyledons folded together in the midst of the floury endosperm. In these seeds the nourishment so necessary for the starting of the young plant on its career is found *around* the embryo, in the endosperm, instead of in the first leaves of the embryo itself. It is digested and absorbed by the young plant during germination; the endosperm becomes gradually more succulent, watery; and finally disappears.

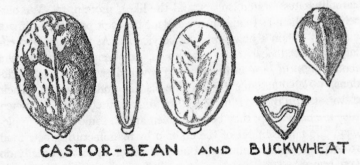

CASTOR-BEAN AND BUCKWHEAT

---

* Which means simply "in the seed" (*endo-* from the Greek word meaning "within"; *sperm* from the word for "seed"). It was called "albumen" in the older books.

As a matter of fact, all seeds have endosperm—at some time in their lives. The seed which you plant, hard, dry, dormant, is the product of development; it has a history. The embryo and the endosperm are the same age and began their growth together; the embryo pushing into the midst of the endosperm and obtaining nourishment from it. The rest of the story varies with the kind of plant. In some the embryo grows the faster, consuming the endosperm, absorbing it, filling its own leaves with the food thus obtained.* This is what happens in a bean, and in the seeds of roses and dahlias and radishes and oak-trees and apples and walnuts. In others the endosperm grows as fast as the embryo and continues to envelop it, at least partly: surrounding it with nutriment.

It is a rather curious fact that such an immense variety of plants, forming seeds of such various appearances, should all have embryos of the same general structure; particularly all having a *pair* of primary leaves. Why just *two* cotyledons? Why not three, or five, or a variable number? The number of petals in the flowers varies; but oaks and maples and violets and sunflowers and roses and lupines and petunias and phlox—all these and many more have seeds with two cotyledons.†

There is, however, one group of plants which departs from this rule. Their species are not so numerous, but they are everywhere in our fields and gardens; they are the grasses, and their relatives the palms and lilies and orchids and others. Their embryos have each but one cotyledon.

The interest and significance of this fact was first announced by the great English botanist John Ray (1627-1705), who based his classification of flowering plants upon it. He made two groups of them, now commonly referred to as the dicots and the monocots,‡ according as their embryos have two cotyledons or one

---

* A common error is to speak of the stem and bud of a bean as constituting the embryo and to consider the cotyledons only as a store of food. Really they are all connected, all parts of the embryo.

† There are occasional exceptions; three or more cotyledons may be found on one stem; but these are obviously abnormal, and do not invalidate the general statement.

‡ Or, more technically, Dicotyledoneae and Monocotyledoneae.

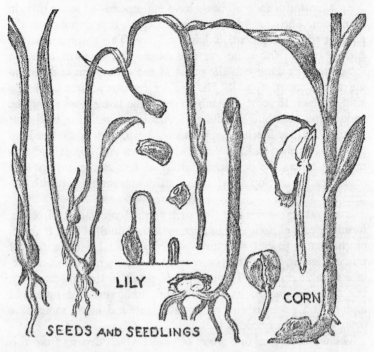

LILY

CORN

SEEDS AND SEEDLINGS

cotyledon respectively. There are numerous other differences between the two groups (for we do not classify by single characters), but this is all that concerns us for the moment. As one of the monocots we may take first the seed of a lily, a flat seed, packed with a hundred others just like it in the pod which succeeds the flower.

This seed contains endosperm, in the midst of which lies the embryo: a small rod, nearly straight. Most of this rod is the single cotyledon (not at all answering to our usual idea of a leaf); its base is a very short stem, at the end of which is the root-tip. The bud is in a pocket at the base of the cotyledon, just where it joins the stem; this opens to one side by a narrow slit. It terminates the stem as usual, but instead of lying between two cotyledons it is enveloped by the single cotyledon, which now *seems* to terminate the stem. When this seed germinates, the root is formed in the usual way, from the lower end of the stem; then both stem and cotyledon elongate, the latter becoming erect, a small green needle standing straight up and carrying on its tip the seed coat and the remains of the endosperm, from which it has drawn much of the food. Later the first bud emerges from the slit in the base of the cotyledon, and the embryo is on its way to becoming a mature lily plant.

The commonest, and to us the most familiar monocots are the grasses; not only the grasses of our lawns and pastures, but also the cereals—wheat, oats, barley, rice, corn, and the rest—and the bamboos; all these compose the great grass family. As we chose a bean to represent seeds in general on account of its large size, for the same reason we may take a grain of corn to illustrate the seed of the grasses.

The embryo or "germ" of the grain is plainly visible even without dissection; it forms a whitish, shield-shaped area just beneath the skin on one side. To study its parts cut through this and through the grain lengthwise in a plane perpendicular to the flat surface. The embryo occupies roughly a half of the cut surface, the endosperm the other half; they are separated by a line running diagonally across the grain. The bud and the primary root may easily be seen just under the skin, the former directed towards the top of the grain. The single large cotyledon arises from the stem at the base of the bud, and almost completely envelops the other parts, forming most of the embryo. If the embryo is dissected out in one piece, only the cotyledon is seen; the bud and root lie in a cavity within it, the only sign of which is a slit at one side.

When this grain germinates, the bud emerges from the soil as a green spike or spear; the lengthening green leaves soon split the sheath which at first encloses them, and spread apart. Besides the primary root, by now deep in the soil, other roots grow out near the base of the bud. The cotyledon, like those of a pea, remains below ground; no extension of the stem lifts it up. It assists in the nourishment of the growing regions, in an important way. It forms the digestive substances known as enzymes (particularly diastase) which pass out into the endosperm and cause the digestion of the starch and other foods therein contained; these are then (and not

until then) capable of being absorbed by the growing embryo.*
Barley grains, which have been soaked so as to initiate their digestive activity, form the malt of commerce, valuable for its
sugars (the products of digestion) and other foods, and as a source
of enzymes.

Even when we extend our view of the processes of germination
to include seeds so widely different from beans as those of lilies
and corn, it is clear that there is a common pattern. All these
embryos† consist of a stemlike part with its two growth-regions:
at one end the part that is to become the root; at the other that
which will add to the stature of the stem and form the new
leaves. The one or two cotyledons assist in the nutrition of the
embryo in a variety of ways, and take a great variety of forms; but
in position they bear the same relation to the other parts. The two
growing tips foreshadow the pattern which runs through the entire
world of flowering plants (and of some other plants besides); for
all these consist essentially of a stem (with or without branches),
leaves borne on the stem, and a root system. Or, to express it
differently, every flowering plant consists of a shoot and a root.
These parts take many forms, and are, indeed, sometimes difficult
to identify. A cactus does not much resemble a duckweed and
neither bears much likeness to a grass or to an oak; but careful
study will confirm the statement made above, that all these plants
are "cut from the same cloth." In the same way you may discover
a common pattern in animals so diverse as seals, birds, horses,
and dogs; many of the same bones may be identified in all these,
and receive the same names.

Of course such wide differences in structure and form are responsible for equally wide differences in habit and behavior. The
seal is at home in the water as the bird is in the air—and as the
horse is in neither. Duckweed and cactus flourish only in their
special environments, and other plants will languish in either. How-

---

* Digestion and enzymes are discussed on p. 88.
† Except for a few oddities such as the embryos of orchids, which are not
formed into parts in the seeds; even in these, however, similar parts do appear,
later, during germination; and the usual pattern is realized.

ever, just as there is one general structural pattern running through the whole array, so there are certain underlying patterns of behavior, of function. All these plants have certain nutritional processes in common; they all live on much the same fare, which they digest and transport from point to point within their bodies and from which they obtain energy and the materials for new growth. And in all of them this complex but fairly uniform economy depends upon water.*

The swelling of the bean when it is wet is a symptom of a relationship which will continue during the life of the plant. The first part to grow, to emerge from the broken seed-coat, is the root, the water-gathering part of the plant; without the water which will be tapped and absorbed by the root, all the activity of stem and leaves would be of no avail, and the life of the young plant would quickly end. This is common knowledge among growers of plants, though they may not always appreciate just what the water is used for in the plant, nor how the plant succeeds in finding it.

HOW ROOTS FIND WATER

Everyone knows that the root finds water by turning *downwards* into the earth. Why does it do so? How does it know where water is likely to be found? Of course the root does not "know," in the sense in which we usually use that word. Still less does it grow "in search of" water, as we are tempted to write. It grows downwards by its own nature, compulsively, unless something interferes. This is a remarkable fact; not always appreciated even by the farmer and the gardener, who drop seed carelessly into the ground without troubling to see that each root-tip points downwards. And facts challenge us; they must have an explanation. What hidden force, what subtle mechanism governs the

---

* Statements about the plant's need for water must be modified for those plants that live actually in the water and under it; but such plants also *use* water; they differ in not having any difficulty in getting it.

growth of these small living tips? What are the *causes* of their bendings and turnings?*

You can place the root of a seedling in any position you wish, in a little moist chamber from which light is excluded; and it will invariably turn downwards as it grows. The bending is not caused by light, for no light reaches it; nor by water, for water reaches it uniformly from all sides. The only thing left, the only thing to which the root is subject that acts in a downward direction, is gravity. It is gravity that causes the root to grow down.

A chemical compound is involved in this action; a compound made in the tip of the root which flows back into the older part, where it influences the lengthening of the root (for a root lengthens a short distance behind the tip). Because of gravity this substance is most active on the *lower* side of a root which extends horizontally, and retards the elongation *of that side*; since the upper side elongates normally the root bends downwards. When the growing part of the root is directed vertically downwards, the growth-regulating substance acts uniformly through it and elongation is equal on all sides (other things being equal). Our knowledge (recently acquired) of such substances answers in a remarkable way our questions about the apparent purposiveness of infant plant parts; but we have still much to learn.

The life-blood of science is its stream of unanswered questions,

---

* The search for causes is one of the trademarks of scientists; it marks the kind of knowledge in which they are interested. Much rather turgid stuff has been written about science and scientists. There is no wizardry in them, no magic, nothing denied to common sense and imagination. Science means knowledge; scientists are persons in possession of knowledge and in search of more. The only thing we must watch is the *kind* of knowledge on which they insist—knowledge which can be tested by "evidence," by "objective" data on which all can agree. That is why we cannot explain the actions of plants by referring to their purposes. Feelings, intuitions, aspirations, purposes, aesthetic judgments—real as they are, these do not qualify as scientific data until we have evidence of their existence which is independent of their supposed effects. We *may* know our own purposes, our own aims; we cannot know those of our fellow creatures unless they tell us. So in seeking what makes a root grow down rather than up or sideways, we look for forces and substances which we can identify, for what we call "mechanical causes," rather than for purposes or intelligence or feelings. The chief justification of such a method of attack on our problems is its success; it has revealed to us much of the working of the living world.

and in any science there are—fortunately—plenty of them. This particular question—about the mechanism of the response to gravity—has been answered only recently, and of course not even yet completely answered. The rapid increase in our knowledge of the way in which the root responds to gravity has resulted, like most progress in science, from the labors of many men. One of the first was Charles Darwin, who in 1880 contributed the interesting fact that a root would fail to respond—that is, it would not grow down if placed in some other direction—after the tip had been cut off. The bending, however, did not take place at the tip, but a short distance behind it. It seemed clear to Darwin that the tip "perceived" the direction of gravity, and an "influence" was "transmitted" to the part that accomplished the bending. For many years thereafter botanists assumed that this "influence" was a current, an electrical change, an irritation, or something equally vague; more or less comparing the process to what takes place in animals—perception by a sensory organ, transmission through nerves, response by muscles—though they knew well enough that no such parts are to be found in plants. Infatuation with words may sometimes be responsible for stagnation in learning.

The next steps were taken in the two decades after 1910. At this time the growing shoot was studied instead of the root; and the response to light instead of the action of gravity. The choice was purely a matter of convenience; it turned out, as will be seen, that the underlying causes of all these phenomena are related. As everyone knows, especially every housewife who grows "house plants," plants turn towards light as they grow. The cause of the bending is the light itself; it does not occur in complete darkness, and a plant in a completely dark box does not "know how" to find its way out even if a way exists. But if you illumine it from any one direction, the plant turns in that direction as it grows. This was the principle used in the experiments. The shoots of oats, projecting only a little from the seed, were illumined from one side. As in the root, it was soon evident that the sensitive part was the extreme tip, and something passed from there to the region below in which the curvature appeared; for if the tip was cut off, the bending did not occur.

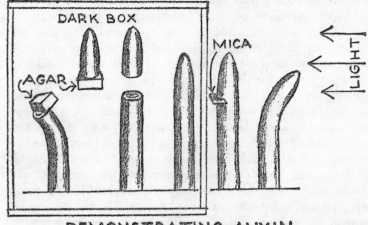

DEMONSTRATING AUXIN

The beginning of a solution of the problem occurred when several men in different countries (Boysen-Jensen, Paal, Went) showed that this "influence" or whatever one chose to call it could not pass through a minute sheet of mica inserted in a cut in the shoot between the tip and the region of bending. It would pass, however, if the entire tip was sliced off and then replaced on the stump. Immediately this suggested that a *substance* was involved: some substance dissolved in the liquids of the plant and moving from the tip towards the base of the shoot.

Moreover, if the tip of a shoot which had never been exposed to light, one-sided light or all-sided, was cut off and then stuck back *on one edge* of the cut surface, the shoot would bend *as if it had been exposed to light from the other side*. Evidently the substance which comes from the tip caused that side into which it passed to grow more than the other side. Finally, if the tip was cut off, and placed with the cut surface downward on a minute block of jelly,* then this bit of jelly acquired the "influence" (in reality, the substance) which causes this effect on growth. It could

---

* Agar was used; a gelatin-like material derived from a seaweed and capable of holding a large amount of water in a "semisolid" condition—and in one position.

be placed on decapitated stumps and would cause them to bend this way or that or to grow straight upwards, at the will of the experimenter, according as he balanced the lump on one edge or the other or placed it in the middle. Whatever was coming from the tip had been trapped in that little block of jelly (essentially a little block of water). There could be no doubt that a substance was involved, a chemical substance, soluble in water and capable of moving through the plant in dissolved form.

At once the problem had a new aspect. Now the chemists could get busy. Hundreds of painstaking experiments and calculations and extractions and analyses were made, and are still being made; our knowledge of the substances involved and of their effects is now extensive, though of course far from complete.

The material which Went caught in his minute lumps of agar has proved difficult to isolate and identify, because of the very small quantities that are present. Several such substances have been named; in general they are called auxin.* One derived, not from the tips of seedlings but from certain fungi was called hetero-auxin, the "different auxin," and was caught in sufficient quantities to be chemically analyzed. The chemist calls it indole-acetic acid (IAA). Recent studies indicate that the auxin which occurs in the tips and in other parts of plants is perhaps also indole-acetic acid.

We now know that auxin (whatever it is chemically) is normally and continually produced, in minute but sufficient quantities, in the growing tips of stems and roots and in young parts generally. It travels back from these extremities into the older parts. If a stem is standing erect and is evenly illuminated from all sides, the influence of the auxin on growth is equal on all sides, and growth is uniform in the stem. But if light comes only from one side, the auxin on that side is apparently partially destroyed; the darker side is thereby stimulated to greater elongation, and bending towards the light results.

If a stem extends horizontally, it bends so as to grow upwards. This is how the first shoot of a corn grain manages to emerge from the ground. Like the downward growth of a root, this action is

---

* From a Greek word meaning "to grow."

directed by gravity. Is this absurd? Can gravity make something go *up*? Of course it can: attach two unequal weights to the two ends of a cord which passes over a pulley; gravity will cause the heavier to descend and therefore the lighter to rise. In the relation of a growing plant with gravity, it is not merely the *force* of gravity that we are concerned with; it is the direction of gravity and the response made by the plant to that directional urge. Gravity causes the auxin, flowing back from the tip of the horizontally placed stem, to accumulate on the lower side or at least to be more active on that side; and this stimulates the lower side to increased elongation, so that the stem bends upwards. When the stem is erect, the auxin is uniformly active (as far as gravity is concerned) and elongation also is uniform on all sides.

Auxin is responsible also for the turnings of a root. But the living substance of a root seems to be more sensitive to it than that of a stem (and even a stem can get too much of it, as will be seen). The same concentration of auxin which *stimulates* stems to elongate *retards* roots in their growth; roots generally bend in the opposite direction—away from light, if they are exposed on one side to light; and downwards, if they are placed in some direction other than vertical. In either case, the side on which the auxin is most active grows less than the other side.

Many factors influence the young root in directing its growth. But the primary urge downwards into the soil and towards the water hidden in the soil is due to gravity; it is accomplished through the production of auxin, and through the movement of auxin away from the tip. The same auxin, the same movement of auxin causes the stem to push its way upwards into the light and the air. The young plant succeeds in orienting itself in its world, not, so far as we can discover, through some purpose with which it is imbued, not because of some "instinct," but through the behavior of certain chemical substances within it.*

* Bendings made by plants in response to factors in their environment are known as tropisms; from a Greek word meaning "to turn." The response to gravity is called geotropism, "earth turning"; the response to light is phototropism, "light turning."

FROM AUXINS TO WEED-KILLERS AND VITAMINS

Now that we have some idea of the chemical nature of auxin (or at least of heteroauxin), we can make a number of substances with similar chemical nature and properties, and apply them to plants—with various results. A plant can get too much auxin. An excess of heteroauxin, indole-acetic acid (commonly abbreviated as IAA), may produce all sorts of abnormal developments, twistings, tumor-like swellings, and so forth. The relatives of auxin are the substances we now use so effectively to eliminate dandelions and plantains from our lawns, and as more or less selective weed-killers in general; we use them in much higher concentrations than any which occur in a living plant, and the result is quite different. The first-known and best-known of them is dichlorophenoxyacetic acid, commonly referred to as 2,4-D and sold under many proprietary names. Trichlorophenoxyacetic acid is also used for certain purposes, and indole-butyric acid and naphthalene-acetic acid and many others. They differ in their effects. The 2,4-D which you apply to your lawn may cause the same sort of overgrowths and malformations in the weeds as IAA does when it is applied to plants in the laboratory. Indole-butyric acid is one of those which may be used to stimulate root formation in cuttings; of course the proper concentration must be used to avoid injury. Hundreds of such compounds are now known, having the most remarkable effects on vegetation; especially remarkable in view of the very low concentrations which will produce them. They may be concerned with normal growth and the bendings which a plant makes; they may stimulate the growth of roots which otherwise do not appear or appear more tardily; they may be used in the production of fruit without seeds; they may cause overgrowths and tumors; they may bring about the death of the plant. The minute quantities that will produce such effects must be emphasized. A nurseryman I know used 2,4-D to eliminate weeds from some of his plantings. Later he used the same spray-tank, which he had thoroughly rinsed out in the usual way, to

apply Bordeaux mixture to his tomatoes. Shortly after this application he was puzzled by the appearance of the tomato leaves:
they were irregularly thickened, crinkled and curled. Later he was
dismayed by the sight of yellowed and dying plants; the entire crop
was a failure. All that damage was caused by the amounts of 2,4-D
which adhered to the smooth walls of a metal tank after it had
been well washed with water.

The fact that auxin and auxin-like substances can interfere
with growth as well as stimulate it leads to yet another class of
substances. It has long been known that certain plants exert a
retarding influence upon the growth of others, presumably through
some substance which they give off in the soil. Certain kinds of
trees, notably the black walnut, are said to prevent the growth of
other plants within a certain distance from their roots. More
recently (and more exactly) it has been shown that fungi have a
definite influence on other fungi and on bacteria, including some
of those which are responsible for our own ailments. Bacteria and
fungi are grown, for purposes of research, in flat circular covered
dishes of glass, called Petri dishes. Usually the substratum is a layer
of agar in which nutrient substances have been dissolved. When
many bacteria are scattered through such a "plate," they grow
into hundreds of small "colonies" visible to the naked eye. But
if a certain kind of fungus is first planted in the plate and allowed
to form a colony, a sort of halo may appear around it; a clear zone
in which the bacteria do not grow. This is the visible evidence of
the production by the fungus of an "antibiotic." Sir Alexander
Fleming observed this effect in a culture-vessel containing a blue
mold named Penicillium. The antibiotic substance which stopped
the bacterial growth was extracted; and so we have penicillin.
This, as everyone knows, was the first of a succession of substances
which have the power of stopping or retarding bacterial growth.
They do it not only in glass dishes but often in the human body;
and, providing they are not themselves injurious, may be used to
retard the development of the diseases caused by some bacteria,
or to prevent them altogether. Some success has been obtained also
in preventing plant diseases with these substances. They are
formed naturally by many plants, including minute fungi which

occur in the soil; but we do not yet understand their part in the economy of nature.

Auxin bears an obvious resemblance to those substances in animals which are responsible for the harmonious growth and functioning of the body—the hormones*; it is sometimes referred to as a phytohormone, plant hormone.† Auxin, the hormones, and other materials, including the weed-killers noticed above, form a category of substances known variously as growth-regulatory substances, growth regulators, or simply growth substances. They are as remarkable for the diversity and magnitude of their effects as for the small quantities which are sufficient to produce them. Perhaps the best known of this group are the vitamins, so familiar now in our own diet. It is common knowledge that the vitamins come mainly from plants. It is not so generally understood that the plants themselves need and use them; if something interferes with the supply their growth is retarded and finally ceases, and death will ensue.

This is a good example of the devious and wholly unforeseeable ways in which human knowledge, science, advances. All this started with Darwin's crude surgery on the tip of a root. From such simple experiments we come, by many stages, to a knowledge of weed-killers, therapeutic drugs, and vitamins.

---

* Derived from a Greek word meaning "to arouse"; hormones are sometimes called "chemical messengers," since they commonly migrate from where they are formed and cause a response in some other part. The resemblance between their history and that of the auxin in a tropism is obvious. In other reactions, however, auxin may have an effect upon the same part in which it is formed; in which case the term hormone is not so readily applicable.

† The Greek word latinized as *phyton* means "plant"; botany has sometimes been called phytology; plant geography is phytogeography; the study of the diseases of plants is phytopathology.

2

How Plants Grow

THE WORLD OF CELLS

In seeking to understand anything, there are two ways of looking at it. One may first scrutinize its form, the parts of which it is composed, the way in which these parts are put together. Or one may ask what it does, how it behaves, in what activities it engages and how it accomplishes them. The study of form is morphology; the study of behavior is physiology.*

Commonly we pursue both sorts of inquiry together, all mixed up; indeed it is scarcely possible to separate them absolutely. Think of an automobile: how can one talk intelligently of the *working* of the distributor without having some slight understanding of its *structure*; or vice versa? The descriptions of seeds in the earlier pages of this book were morphological; but when we strayed into a discussion of their germination—that was physiology. Morphology by itself may be, at least to many persons, rather dreary. Physiology by itself may be largely incomprehensible. When the two work together, both are illumined.

Now therefore, before going further into the behavior of plants, we must inquire a little more closely into their physical composition. Only thus may we gain a clearer picture of just *how* a root, for instance, becomes longer, *how* it bends, *how* it is changed from an embryonic to a mature body, *how* it can transport water and food and do all the things that the living root does.

---

* And the words are extended to mean not only "the study of" but also the results of such study. When we speak of the morphology of a plant we mean its structure as elucidated by morphological study.

It is unfortunate that the parts of living things are minute; not so small as the atoms and electrons of chemistry, but still invisible to ordinary sight. We must magnify them in order to see them; we must study them with microscopes.

We can obtain some preliminary notion of the structure of plants by using the very small roots which emerge from some of the smaller grass seeds. They are so slender and so transparent that an entire root may be mounted in water* on a glass "slide" and, with a little manipulation of the apparatus, almost every minute part may be brought into view.

The most obvious fact about such a root, apparent at first glance, is that it is entirely divided into a great number of small squares and oblongs, as they appear in microscopic view; but they have depth as well, so that they are really like minute boxes or compartments—cells. Over the extreme tip of the rootlet is a thimble-like cap, similarly constructed of cells; some of these are loose and tend to float off as soon as the root is placed in water. The actual growing tip of the root, just inside this cap, may appear greenish or yellowish and rather opaque as compared with the rest of the root; the cells, very small, are hard to make out. As the eye travels back from this tip region, the cells are seen to be longer and longer, and more transparent; and they are quite evidently in

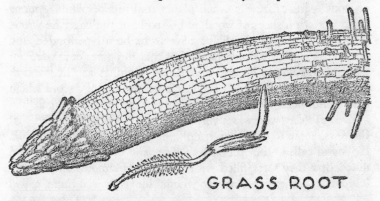

GRASS ROOT

---

* Objects to be studied with the microscope must generally be mounted in a liquid; otherwise light is refracted from their surfaces and one gets only a distorted image.

rows or files which extend the length of the root and converge in
the tip. Farther away from the tip there are transparent threads
or hairs which project sidewise from the surface of the root into
the water; these are easily seen to be extensions of some of the
surface cells. All the root, in fact, is made of cells: the root-cap, the
tip region, the region where the cells are longer, the hairs; there is
nothing there except cells; and the cells all fit rather closely together, with little evidence of any spaces between them. Clearly
whatever the root *does* is accomplished by the cells; the behavior of
the root is to be understood in terms of the activities of its cells.

This remarkable state of things has not been known very long;
the study of cells* is one of the younger branches of biology, being
dependent upon the use of a microscope. Although single lenses
were known in antiquity, compound microscopes were not in-
vented until late in the sixteenth century, and came into use only
in the seventeenth. An Englishman named Robert Hooke, a
member of the newly formed Royal Society, enjoyed experimenting
with these new devices, as gentlemen of parts and leisure often
enjoyed the pursuit of knowledge. In 1665 he brought out a book,
entitled *Micrographia: or some Physiological Description of Minute Bodies made by Magnifying Glasses*. It contains descriptions
and illustrations of a great variety of things, pieces of metal and
of stone, parts of insects, small plants, and bits of plants. Among
them were thin slices of wood and of cork; of the latter he wrote,
"I could exceeding plainly perceive it to be all perforated and
porous, much like a Honey-comb, but that the pores of it were not
regular." Elsewhere he speaks of these openings as "little boxes
or cells." This is apparently the first botanical use of a word which
is now indispensable to the vocabulary of the biologist: "cell."

Even Hooke (who was a very indifferent scientist) realized that
there was more to cells than simply the "pores" in a piece of cork.
He found cells also in the pith of elder and of various herbs, and
noted that they were filled with "juices." His more famous con-
temporary, Nehemiah Grew, to whom Hooke showed them, called

---

* Cytology; the word is derived from the Greek word meaning "sac," since
living cells may be thought of in this way. They are closed sacs containing
liquids.

these sometimes "Bubles," sometimes "Bladders." Marcello
Malpighi, who shares with Grew the honor of having laid the
foundations of plant anatomy, wrote his great work in Latin and
called these little objects *utriculi*, which means small sacs or bags.
It was not until much later that the word "cell" gradually took
precedence over "bladders," "vesicles," and the like; and it was not
until the beginning of the nineteenth century that men began to
realize how important they are. It was some time before they
grasped the fact that the pores in wood, the vesicles in pith, and
the fibers and ducts of plants are all essentially of the same nature:
they are all cells or strips of cells. Still later did they recognize
that the same is true of animals, and that the cells of plants and
of animals are essentially the same. A world of cells! Just as to
the chemist the universe is composed of complex swarms of invisible but active molecules and atoms and electrons and so on; so
the biologist has become used to thinking of living things as
conglomerations of cells, of cells of many and various types,
arranged in complex patterns, carrying on the numerous and complicated activities that make up—life.

Of course when we speak in this way of cells we are not thinking
merely of the *walls* that make up the compartments we see; it is
the "juices" inside that command our interest. It is the matter
within the walls that is really *alive*. If we return to the root and
examine some of the cells on the surface with a somewhat higher
magnification, we can make out some of the details and properties
of these "juices." And through such studies—and again through
the use of painstaking and skillful techniques developed through
several generations of microscopists—we have acquired a vast
knowledge of the contents of living cells.

The living material of cells has been named protoplasm. It is
not really much like a "juice"; it is not a watery solution, able to
pass unchanged through a chemist's filter-paper. It is what the
chemist and physicist call a colloid. A colloid is composed of various kinds of molecules* grouped into minute droplets (too small
for the microscope) immersed in a liquid. It is nearly colorless,
somewhat viscous, often in motion, usually containing within its

---

* A molecule is the smallest unit in which a substance can retain its identity.

VACUOLE   NUCLEUS   CYTOPLASM

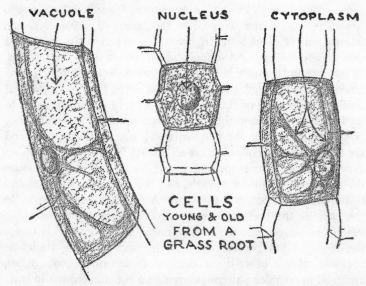

CELLS
YOUNG & OLD
FROM A
GRASS ROOT

meshes droplets of water, globules of oil, minute crystals, and other microscopic bodies. Water is often conspicuously collected in parts called vacuoles.* In an older cell, indeed, most of the water runs together in a large central vacuole; the more viscous protoplasm surrounds this, always lining the cell wall.

The protoplasm almost always includes a small body called the nucleus: enormously important, for, as will be seen later (p. 134), it controls the destiny of the cell. The protoplasm *forms* everything: the wall around itself, the colors which delight you in your garden, the leaves and flowers and fruits in infinite variety; it moves and grows and accomplishes various bendings and twistings. The word itself means "first former." And all these manifold activities are governed by the nucleus. The rest of the protoplasm, called the cytoplasm, cannot long survive if the nucleus is removed; and is quite unable to develop, to grow. It is also true that the nucleus cannot live without some cytoplasm around it; it is not independent; the cytoplasm contributes to its support and activity.

---

* *Vacuus* in Latin means "empty." A vacuole, however, is not really empty; but water being transparent, it appears so when seen in the microscope.

These two, nucleus and cytoplasm, are inseparable,* mutually dependent, partners in the business of living.

The protoplasm is alive; it is *in it* that the formation of new living matter occurs, the formation of auxin, of enzymes, of many other things; the many and complex changes that lead to the development of the plant (or animal), all its parts and colors and odors. We know something of the physical and chemical makeup of protoplasm; but we do not know it all, and it is so complex that we perhaps never shall.

The vacuole or vacuoles are composed mainly of water, in which salts or sugars or colored materials may be dissolved. They seem inert; but there is a frequent interchange between vacuole and surrounding protoplasm, and to that extent the vacuoles share in the life of the cell. Indeed, the vacuole is sometimes and by some botanists considered a part of the protoplasm; by others it is listed separately among the constituents of the cell.

Such are the "juices" of which Hooke and Grew wrote, which inhabit the "bubbles" or "bladders" or "cells" which compose the softer parts of plants and animals. Each of these is itself a small organism: it has a structure. Each cell consists (so far as it is alive) of protoplasm. The protoplasm consists of a nucleus surrounded by cytoplasm. There are one or more vacuoles.

Around the protoplasm is the wall, formed by the living matter, enclosing it in a usually transparent envelope, composed primarily of cellulose. It is penetrated by very minute pores by means of which the protoplasm of adjoining cells is connected; so that the division of a plant or animal into a multitude of separate units is more apparent than real. The wall is usually said to be nonliving; it is certainly relatively inert; but it is difficult to draw boundaries around living activities.

The curious thing is that the word "cell" has not only outlasted all the others but has so changed its original meaning that it applies not only to the walls but also to the liquids contained by those walls. There are even "cells" without walls, if such an absurdity can be admitted; for there are among plants and animals many small bits of protoplasm which can swim or drift about in the

---

* With a few interesting exceptions; see p. 90.

waters of the earth enclosed in nothing but the living membranes at their surface. These also are cells, in the sense of the biologist; each is a protoplasmic unit, a body of cytoplasm containing a nucleus; what is often called a protoplast. But at the same time biologists, with a certain characteristic inconsistency, continue to use the word also for the cavities in cork and wood with their enclosing walls—cavities which once contained living protoplasm but do so no longer. When you meet the word "cell," then, the context must help you decide just what it means at the moment: protoplasmic unit, protoplast, with or without enclosing wall; or wall, with or without enclosed protoplasm.

When one has listened to lectures on cells or studied them in textbooks, still more when one has become expert in the use of a microscope and has spent many hours and days looking through it at parts of plants and animals, one is apt to forget how small, and how numerous, cells are. In the "high power" of an ordinary student microscope the entire field of view may be less than half a millimeter across (a millimeter is about the twenty-fifth part of an inch); and in this space there are many cells. Ordinary cells of plants vary in diameter from about a hundredth to a tenth of a millimeter. An apple of average size may contain fifty million cells. One leaf from the tree on which it grows has about as many. If we estimate roughly the number of apples and the number of leaves on the tree, and add something for the trunk and branches and the root system, we arrive at the astonishing total of twenty-five quadrillions. Such figures are trivial, of course, to the chemist and physicist, who deal with atoms and molecules and electrons and stars; but they are sufficiently startling as representing the quantities of actual living units of which familiar plants and animals are made. When you bite into an apple you may have a mouthful of a million cells!

GROWTH OF A ROOT

A root, then, growing out from a bean or a grain of corn or a grass seed or any seed at all is made of cells. The stem also is made of cells, and so are the leaves. Where did they all come from? They were not all there in the embryo before germination. It is true that the embryo was made of cells; but not that many. The solution is found in the remarkable capacity of cells for multiplication. They multiply by division. By building a wall across a room we can divide it into two rooms; and cell division is something like that. But it is not so simple; it is a most intricate process, the details of which must be deferred until a later page (p. 131); it must suffice here to mention briefly its main features. *The nucleus of the parent cell is itself first divided into two nuclei*, each identical in the fine details of its structure with the parent nucleus, but about half the size. These move apart, and a new wall is formed between them. In this way two cells have their origin, each complete with nucleus and cytoplasm—the indispensable parts. Together they occupy the space taken by the parent cell. Each daughter cell may now enlarge until it is as big as the parent cell, and then repeat the process. In this way one cell may finally give rise to a group of cells, which will continue to enlarge almost indefinitely. *The cells are formed two at a time**; each parent cell divides into two, which themselves become the parents of the next division.

The root, however, is not just a mass of minute cells, all alike, all dividing to form new cells. Even a glance will show you that only the extreme tip is like this. The rest of the root is made of larger cells, most of which do not divide; they are obviously of several different kinds, arranged mostly in rows which extend lengthwise through the root, in a definite pattern. How does this pattern, this structure evolve? How does an embryo plant, composed of cells which are all much alike in size and shape, become a growing plant composed of many distinct kinds of cells?

It is not difficult to understand how the root becomes an elongated structure, its cells arranged in rows. In that apical region, that mass of minute cells which are all much alike and mostly dividing, most of the walls which separate the new cells are perpendicular to the length of the root; a succession of divisions of this kind, all in parallel planes, will inevitably create a row or file of cells arranged end to end. As these rows of cells are formed, en-

---

* In the usual course of events. In the reproduction of certain plants other methods of division occur.

largement occurs to a greater degree in some cells than in others. The cells at the extreme apex of the root usually enlarge only until they approximately equal the parent cell in size; then they themselves divide. But the cells farther away from the tip become much longer than the parent cells by which they were formed; they may be several times as long before they divide. Some become longer than others; some cells in the files near the center of the root continue to lengthen while their neighbors are still dividing. All this accounts for that part of the root just above the tip in which the cells are longer than those in the tip itself, and become longer and longer the farther they are from the tip. These cells were formed, by division, in the tip itself a short time before you see them; they have lengthened, with a partial cessation or slowing-down of division. This has two notable effects on the life and growth of the root. First, the region of actively dividing cells does not get much larger, since some of the products of division are always ceasing to be a part of it. Second, the tip of the root (covered by its thimble-like cap) is pushed ahead—into the earth, if the root is growing in its normal environment—by the lengthening of the cells behind it.

So it goes—potentially a never-ending process. The apical region does not become appreciably larger, in spite of the multiplication of its cells; the "surplus" cells are added to the length of the root. A root increases in length *only near the tip*; not exactly at the tip. Division of cells becomes rarer and finally ceases altogether as cells become older and larger. Finally enlargement also ceases, as if the cells had reached their utmost capacity. Above the part in which cells are elongating there is very little division, very little change in size.* In this upper, older part the cells undergo other changes, of the utmost complexity and importance; changes which transform them into various types of cells, with various peculiarities, performing various functions in the life of the plant; changes which, in short, *differentiate* them.

The apical region where division of cells is continually occurring (or, during a period of dormancy, where this activity is merely sus-

---

* Until another process, called secondary thickening, begins; but that is another story, which begins on p. 111.

pended) is called a meristem.* It must be borne in mind, how-ever, that definitions of parts of living things are seldom capable of precise application. There is no sharp line between the apical meristem and the region of elongation just above it. Some cell division occurs in the latter, and a certain amount of elongation of cells occurs in the meristem.

The meristem also supplies the auxin which is so concerned with the direction and regulation of growth. Some of the chemical processes of those tiny active microcosms result in the production of these potent substances, in minute but sufficient quantities. The auxin flows back from the meristem into the region of elongation and exerts its influence upon the cells there as they become longer —retarding their growth if it reaches a certain concentration. If the root is unaffected by one-sided pulls of gravity or by inequalities in the distribution of water and other things, the auxin flows equally through the root, and all cells are affected in the same way. But if the root is horizontal or otherwise exposed to some one-sided influence of its environment, the auxin likewise becomes one-sided in its distribution; it becomes more concentrated on one side than on the other, and the cells on that side are retarded in their elonga-tion, so that a bending occurs.

It is now plain why the bending of the root takes place only at a short distance behind the tip; neither at the tip itself nor in older parts. The bending is caused by inequality in the elongation of the two sides of the root. After all the cells have finished their elongation and begun to mature, the bend is more or less perma-nent; it cannot be reversed. The root will not bend again at the same point. If some new stimulus again causes a bending, the new curve will be in the region where cells are *now* elongating, not where they have already accomplished their elongation and have matured. The bending of the parts of plants is not (in general) comparable to the flexing of our own arms and legs, which is accomplished by the contraction of muscles; the same muscles can contract and relax time after time, and the limb moves back and forth at the same joint.

The possession of meristems (and there are others, elsewhere

* From a Greek word meaning "divisible."

in the plant, besides those at the apices of roots; as will be seen) is one of the striking differences between ordinary plants and ordinary animals (the so-called higher animals, by which we mean those we consider nearest to ourselves). Animals lack such groups of cells at their extremities—regions in which new cells are constantly being formed and added to the length or breadth of those parts. They do not continue to grow indefinitely throughout the growing season and year after year, as plants do—until some circumstance interferes; *all* their cells (except certain layers and zones which take care of wear and tear) eventually cease dividing and assume their characteristic sizes and shapes.

Take one more look at the living grass root; one conspicuous feature has not yet been accounted for. You will notice that the cells of the region of elongation are more transparent than those of the meristem. The latter is granular in appearance, more or less opaque; the elongating part consists largely of the "juices" seen by the old microscopists. Actually the difference is caused by the proportion of water in the protoplasm. Closer scrutiny reveals that —as has already been mentioned—each elongated cell consists largely of a relatively enormous vacuole, which was not present when the cell was meristematic. The vacuole is transparent; it is really water—not pure water, but water containing a very dilute solution of certain salts and other substances. There is not much more of the viscous part of the protoplasm in the enlarged cell than in the meristematic cell; it is distended, spread out in a thin layer next to the wall, by the accumulation of water in the center; it is this water that accounts for the enlargement. If you weigh a dry seed, then plant it and allow the seedling to grow for a week or two; if you then lift the seedling and the remains of the seed, chop them up and place them in an oven which will drive off all the water in them—the second weight will be no more than the first. All that first increase of size, that sprouting and turning and putting forth, all were made by virtue of water taken in, water visibly accumulated in the vacuoles of the cells. On a previous page I said that what a *root* does must be thought of as what all its *cells* do. The water which you are careful to supply your germinating seeds is to be found, after a short time, in the vacuoles of the cells, which are thereby enlarged.

The water comes in with considerable force. A common laboratory demonstration is to place some dry seeds in a jar of water and arrange things so that they can only expand by lifing a weight; they lift it. The water with which germinating seeds and, later, growing root-tips are surrounded forces its way into their cells. We can make a rough comparison by likening the cell to an automobile tire being inflated by an inrush of air.

The processes which cause the entrance of water into cells are complex. Cell walls take up water by imbibition, as gelatin does; the water enters the minute spaces of the substance and causes it to swell and soften. This action is concerned in the absorption of water by seed coats, which are composed largely of cell walls. Water enters the living protoplasm by a process called osmosis, which is briefly discussed on p. 70. Such physical processes are apparently competent to explain the entrance of water into plants and the pressures which are generated within them; we need not invoke any will, any purposeful absorption by the plant, any *need* for water as the *cause* for its taking-up though such need may actually exist.

GROWTH OF A STEM

As the root burrows its way down, the stem aspires upwards. It is curious that its cells behave differently from those of the root, for all came originally from the same beginning, the same single cell, in fact; but so it is. Indeed this is the greatest unsolved riddle of biology: what causes cells to differentiate? The cells of the first bud of the embryo respond otherwise to gravity and light than do those of the root-tip at the other end of the primary stem, though the auxin to which they respond is apparently the same in both. And the final result of the growth of the stem is different: green leaves spreading to the light.

The underlying mechanism of growth is much the same in a stem-tip as in a root-tip. At the tip is a meristem, like that of the tip of the root. In fact, the growth of the embryo (which once con-

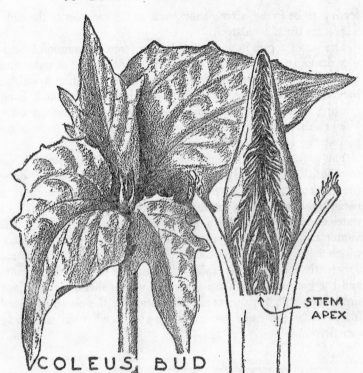

STEM
APEX

COLEUS BUD

sisted entirely of meristematic cells) may be thought of as a separation of these two meristems, one at either end of the primary stem, by the enlargement and maturation of the cells which lie between them.

The apical meristem of the stem is broader than that of the root; the region of elongation is usually much longer. The cells are in files or columns, as in a root; they converge into the tip in much the same way, with most of the divisions perpendicular to the length of the stem. In the tip itself the pattern of divisions, the arrangement of the planes of division, is quite complicated, and different in different kinds of plants. Cells in the extreme tip may divide in such a direction as to add new cells to the outer skin of the stem, while other cells, within these, may be responsible for

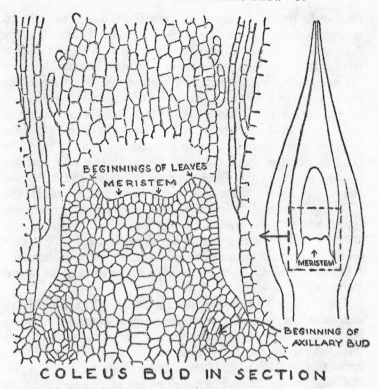

BEGINNINGS OF LEAVES
MERISTEM

MERISTEM

BEGINNING OF
AXILLARY BUD

COLEUS BUD IN SECTION

additions to the inner tissues; so that there is a complex zoned structure in the meristem itself. In general, the cells of the tip retain their characteristic propensity for division and redivision, at least during the growing season; those of their daughter cells which lie on the lower margins of the meristem tend to enlarge more and divide less, gradually forming a region of elongation; just as in a root.

But the growth of a stem is enormously complicated by the formation of leaves. We may think of leaves as things that grow along the sides of the branches; flat, delicate, green objects often on long or short stalks, singly or in pairs or clusters. But to understand where they come from we must look at the tip of the stem, at the apical meristem; for *leaves are formed at the tip*, at the same

time as the length of stem which bears them. Not at the extreme
summit, but a very short distance from it, some of the cells newly
formed by division will begin to divide and enlarge in such a
manner that they form, not a file of cells extending lengthwise in
the stem, but a small projection, a lump of cells which stands out
from the surface. As these cells continue to divide and enlarge,
they become a small plate of cells which stands more or less at
right angles to the surface. A certain inequality in their growth,
however, causes them to curve in their development, so that they
bend in over the tip of the stem. By the time a little leaf has
reached this stage, the tip of the stem, continuing in its normal
course, has formed more cells, has grown broader and a little
higher; and some of the newly formed cells in turn form minute
leaves—nearer to the tip than the one first formed. So the apex of
a stem is covered by successive layers of tiny leaves, the older ones
on the outside and reaching upward and inward so as to cover the
inner ones, and all together covering and enclosing the apical
meristem.

This is a bud. This complex structure, beautifully and symmetri-
cally formed of successively overlapping young leaves and including
the apical meristem of a stem—all this is comprised in that simple
three-letter word. Any bud is potentially a length of stem with the
leaves that will adorn it. As the cells lengthen, forming a region
of elongation, the leaves which were at first so close-packed at the
tip become separated. The cells which were once included in the
short, broad meristem of the apex now form the length of stem
beneath the tip; and the leaves which were once crowded on the
apex are now attached on the sides of this length of stem, often at
wide intervals. Meanwhile the meristem is busy forming yet more
minute leaves overlapping the tip in the same fashion; there is still
a bud at the apex; and, if growth is continuous, as it may be in
plants which grow in an unchanging environment, the terminal
bud is constantly renewed as its lower leaves spread apart.*

But most buds do not grow in a constant environment; they are

---

* A crude idea of a bud is afforded by a head of cabbage or a Brussels
sprout; the leaves enlarged but the stem did not lengthen. Compare also the
bulbs described and illustrated on pp. 102, 103.

exposed to variations in light, temperature, and moisture. In our climate here in New York, and throughout much of the civilized world (a climate called temperate but embracing the most intemperate extremes of heat and cold), buds which endure through the winter begin their growth in spring. Most of them cease growing again early in the summer. Elongation then ceases, and the tiny leaves at the apex fail to separate, the inner ones remaining very small. The outer enveloping leaves of the bud mature without enlarging greatly; in fact, the blades of these leaves may never develop. They become hard-coated, tightly fitted together, often cemented together, so protecting the inner delicate parts from the dry air which would otherwise wither them in the winter.* Then, in spring, with the sudden rush of water to the tips of the branches, these bud scales are forced apart, the cells of the stem-tip lengthen, separating the leaves, and the meristem begins the formation of the new bud which will open in the following spring. A ring of scars at the base of the new branchlet marks the point from which it originates; they are left by the fallen bud-scales.

Many buds are more complicated than the above description. There may be buds within buds—a whole cluster of buds enclosed within one protective envelope of bud-scales. And buds may contain other things than leaves. The leaves may be replaced by the parts of a flower, which spring from the apical meristem of the stem in much the same way as leaves do. For that reason (and others) the parts of a flower are themselves usually considered to be essentially leaves. So when the terminal bud opens in the spring on a magnolia branch, we see the spreading petals of the flower instead of green leaves. Or a cluster of flowers may emerge, as in a lilac. When a flower replaces the ordinary vegetative parts, elongation of that stem ceases. The formation of the floral parts involves, finally, all the apical meristem, and none is left to continue growth. One complex bud, however, may contain both flower-buds and leaf-buds; each bud, of either kind, is constituted in the same basic pattern, that outlined in the preceding pages. If the growth of the

---

* Not from cold. Resistance to cold is another matter, involving the contents of cells, their chemistry and physics. Cold injury is usually due to the formation of ice in or between living cells.

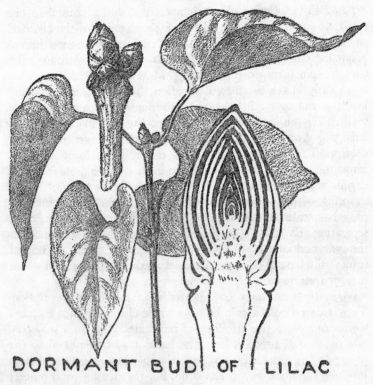

DORMANT BUD OF LILAC

stem is curtailed by the appearance of flowers, it is usually continued by the activity of lateral buds further down; of which more is written below.

BRANCHING OUT

There is a further complication in the growth of a stem—a very important one. The lengthening of the stem is due, of course, to the lengthening of its cells; and as the cells lengthen they gradually cease dividing, finally cease even lengthening, and become mature cells of various kinds. So we might expect a branch, with the leaves along its sides, to be a relatively static thing, incapable, under ordinary circumstances, of further growth. But at every point where a leaf springs from the stem, in the angle or axil formed by the leaf and the stem,—at every such point a small patch of cells *fails to enlarge*; these cells retain their meristematic quality, and continue to divide as the cells around them go about their various business. Each small detached meristem becomes organized into a bud (or perhaps several buds) essentially like that at the apex of the stem: a rounded apical meristem enveloped in small meristematic leaves.

One may see these lateral buds in the axils of the leaves and, after the leaves have fallen, just above the leaf-scars. In some kinds of plants they continue to grow, forming branches that spring from the axils of the leaves; this is often seen in coleus. More usually the axillary buds become dormant; on a perennial stem they may lie dormant for the winter, resuming growth next spring; or they may lie dormant for the rest of their lives. In many plants, indeed, the terminal bud exerts a repressive influence upon the lateral buds; one effect of the auxin which emanates from it is to prevent the lateral buds from developing further. If the terminal bud is removed, by man or by nature, one or more of the lateral buds springs to renewed activity; usually those nearest the tip. Everyone has seen a tree that has lost the end of its main stem in a severe storm and in which a lateral bud has taken over, forming what seems to be a continuation of the truncated stem. In some plants, indeed, such as elm and lilac (here illustrated), the terminal bud is not renewed after the season's growth; one of the uppermost lateral buds, situated very close to the tip, takes its place and forms the stem and leaves of the following season.

This is the origin of the branches of a stem. The cells from which they spring are formed, with the leaves, at the tip of the main stem; and they are arranged in the same way as the leaves are arranged. Look at an ash or maple, which has leaves in pairs; its branches also are in pairs. The branches of an oak arise singly, like the leaves. The lateral buds of a willow may lie dormant for many years, so that no branches may appear on a long stem.

In the fall, when growth and most other activities have ceased (or nearly ceased) in plants and when the leaves are falling, we cut off large parts of our rosebushes. This does not reduce the growth of the following year, but actually enhances it. We remove terminal buds, and we are careful to cut just above axillary buds; the latter, next spring, will unfold into new life. When our flowering shrubs of forsythia and the like end their display early in the season, we remove the older branches, knowing that they will quickly be replaced by the growth of lateral buds. We mercilessly crop the privet, cutting off thousands of terminal buds and thereby stimulating the growth of other thousands of lateral buds which will form the thick screen of short branches which we want. During the summer we pinch off the ends of the chrysanthemums so that more branches will spring forth and the plants will be bushier, with more ends on which to form flowers. We shape our dahlias by favoring certain lateral buds. Much of the art of pruning is based on the existence of buds in the plant, buds which would otherwise be kept dormant by the terminal buds.

Besides the terminal and axillary buds normally present, other buds may be formed, particularly under the influence of wounding and other unusual events, but often without any such stimuli. These are called adventitious buds: chance buds, as it were. They may appear anywhere on a stem—or even on a root.* Their activity is a familiar feature of the "regeneration" of the stump of a felled tree; old tissues which spring into new youth under the influence of rough treatment.

There are many objects in pruning. One of the commonest has been suggested above: to shape plants to our desires. We want our hedges thick, many-branched. We may even clip them into fanciful forms, birds and beasts and purely formal shapes, an art that was familiar to the Romans two thousand years ago. We shape the trees in our orchards so that the crop may be more easily harvested. If we want to grow trees against the house, we can select just the buds we wish to grow, and tie the branches in the shape we want, so forming an espalier tree. We prune apple trees so that one branch does not shade another, for sunlight ripens the fruit. On the other hand, avocados do not ripen well in strong light, and the trees are grown so as to form a dense canopy of

---

* Here growth passes into reproduction—the formation of new plants; under which head adventitious parts are considered further (pp. 120, 123).

leaves. Pear trees are subject to a disease called blight, which spreads from branch to branch if they come in contact with each other. It is well, therefore, to prune pear trees so that they make a loose, open type of growth. We head back trees and shrubs when we transplant them, so as to reduce the area of leaves which will lose water to the air (see p. 54).

Much of our pruning has to do with flowering. Forsythia, lilac, and other shrubs flower on branches which appeared during the preceding season. The growth of new flowering branches is stimulated by removal of the old branches as soon as they have finished flowering. On the other hand, the hybrid tea roses, hydrangeas, and other shrubs form flowers on new growth of the current season; they may be pruned in winter or spring without destroying flower buds. Apple blossoms come from a special sort of bud formed on short branches called spurs; pruning is directed towards favoring the production of spurs and discouraging too great a growth of the long vegetative branches. In growing grapes, we save a few branches for the following year, removing all the rest. The lateral buds on these form new branches, on which flowers and fruit appear during the same season. By thus regulating the number and position of fertile branches we can train them in desirable positions, and get the best possible clusters of grapes.

Pruning is apt to be controversial, some persons advocating pruning in winter, others favoring summer; some pruning excessively, others using the shears more sparingly. Undoubtedly different methods are adapted to different climates as well as to different kinds of plants. But all are based on the botanical facts outlined in the preceding pages: the formation of buds of various types, and the influence exerted by one bud upon another.

Roots usually have no buds, either terminal or axillary. How then do they branch? The earth is certainly full of a tangle of roots; they branch even more abundantly than do stems. The branches are formed in a manner entirely different from those of a stem. Branch roots do not arise at the tip of the parent root, but in the older, mature part. And they have their origin in a group of cells which is found *within* the root, not on its surface. The new apical meristem which is to form a branch root arises from certain interior cells of the parent root and, as it lengthens and forms a region of elongation, *bores its way out* to the surface, destroying some of the cells in its path. The branches are not arranged in a definite pattern on a root as they are on a stem.

3

Water in Plants

WHAT'S IN A LEAF?

Much of the earth is clothed in a mantle of leaves. Leaves are the most familiar of the gifts of nature. Innumerable blades of grass yield to our feet. The foliage of maples and elms and palms rustles in the breeze over our streets. Other leaves wall in our gardens and bound our fields and lanes. Countless leaves canopy the great forests and soften the outlines of mountains. Leaves spread green surfaces to the light and air which nourish them, droop flaccid in a drought, color with magnificent reds and yellows when the nights grow cool, fall dry to the ground and disappear into loam, spring again from a million million buds. Moreover they are interesting not merely as an adornment of the earth; upon them depend not only the lives of the plants which bear them but those of the birds which flutter among them, the worms which crawl upon them, the hoofed animals which graze them, the beasts of prey which stalk those animals, and finally ourselves who slaughter the beasts and cultivate leafy crops—all these depend upon leaves for continued life. If we relapse for a moment into the sort of thinking about plants which we have abjured on a previous page, if we speak of plants as animated by purposes and of their lives as understandable in terms of those purposes, we shall have to say that the main purpose of the young plant whose growth we have followed from embryo towards maturity is to form leaves, to spread them out in the air and light, and to supply them with water. Unscientific as such a statement is, it yet expresses the importance of leaves in the economy of the plant.

Leaves are of many sizes and shapes and vary also in texture.

47

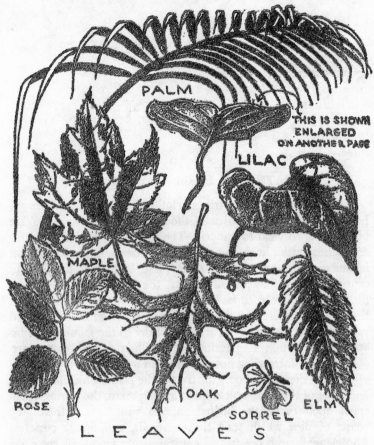

PALM

THIS IS SHOWN
ENLARGED
ON ANOTHER PAGE

LILAC

MAPLE

ROSE

OAK

SORREL

ELM

L E A V E S

The blade of a banana leaf may be six feet long, without the stalk. Some of the weeds which grow in your lawn may have leaves measuring a quarter-inch or less in length. Leaves may be long and narrow like those of grass or round like those of a nasturtium. They are smooth-edged like those of a lilac or toothed like those of a rose; or they may be notched as geranium leaves are notched, or variously lobed, cut, or divided, as leaves of oaks, of larkspur, of lupine are. Some leaves are cut into an infinity of tiny parts so as to be almost feathery in structure; the large leaves of ferns are formed in this way; and the name of the group to which they belong was derived from the Greek word for a wing. Leaves are characteristically green; but many are attractively marked with patches or patterns of red or yellow or bronze; partly for this reason we share our homes with coleus and begonias. Others again have stripes or blotches or margins of white or yellow. Most red or purplish leaves actually contain the same green pigment as ordinary green leaves, masked by the other colors. Occasional yellow and white leaves really lack green; but these are to be regarded as freaks of cultivation, not likely to persist in nature. Most leaves are very thin in proportion to their length and breadth; but crassula, sedum, live-forever, aloe, agave are thick and succulent. With the exception of this group, leaves are surprisingly uniform in their construction; and even the succulents differ rather in degree than in fundamental plan. They all work in much the same way. If we study, say, a leaf of lilac we shall know the essentials of most leaves.

A lilac leaf is a green blade shaped more or less like the conventional picture of a heart, measuring about 4 inches long by 3 inches wide at the widest part, and less than the hundredth part of an inch thick, except where the larger veins project; all this fastened at one end to a slender stalk two or three inches long. A strong vein flows from the stalk into the blade and passes down its middle to the apex; it stands out from the surface of the blade on its lower side, forming a midrib. Other veins branch from this, and a network of still smaller veins arises from these secondary veins, dividing the entire blade into small areas of approximately the same size. The parts that we are first concerned with are these small areas of blade; the structure and functions of veins will come later.

Notice that all this is *leaf*; both blade and stalk may be traced back to one of those small projections from the apical meristem described on page 38. For this reason it is improper to confuse the *stalk* of the leaf with the *stem* from which it arises; they are structurally different also.*

Most mature leaves have no meristems; when they are fully grown they add no more parts. The leaves of grasses are exceptions

---

* The leaf-stalk is technically known as the petiole, from a Latin word which means a small foot or leg.

to this; they have meristems at the base of the blade, which account for their ability to continue growth after they have been mowed.

For all the paper-thinness of the blade, the parts which do the work of a leaf are *inside*. Even the green color is inside—not spread on the surface like paint. There is room within the thickness of the blade for several tiers of cells, rather large cells indeed for cells (a large cell will run to a diameter of a tenth of a millimeter— 1/250 of an inch). These interior cells are enclosed, top and bottom, in a colorless layer, a sort of envelope made of two transparent membranes fastened together at their edges. It is often possible to peel off portions of this colorless, transparent envelope or skin.* The exposed interior of the leaf will then appear dark green and glistening. The outer layer, the skin, is called the epidermis.† For all its diaphanous appearance, it too is composed of cells, and is alive. The interior of the blade is named the mesophyll.‡

It is easy to strip off a small portion of the epidermis, to lay it in a drop of water on a glass slide, to cover it with another piece of glass, and to examine it through a microscope. One's

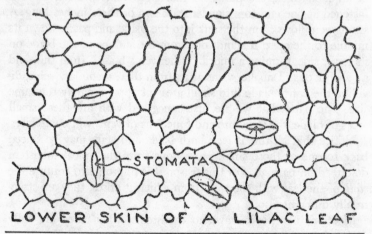

LOWER SKIN OF A LILAC LEAF

* Especially if the leaf is first chilled in a refrigerator.
† The Greek word *epi* here signifies "outer"; "dermis" comes from the word for "skin."
‡ *Mesos* in Greek means "middle"; "phyll" is from the word for "leaf."

first impression is that its cells rather resemble the pieces of a jigsaw puzzle. They are flat, with wavy outlines. They fit closely together; there are no spaces between these pieces, none missing. Here and there, however, especially if you have a bit of epidermis from the lower surface of the leaf, you will see pairs of cells of a different type. They are smaller and somewhat crescent-shaped, or perhaps banana-shaped, and the surprising thing about them is that they do *not* fit closely together. They always occur in pairs, and the two cells of each pair lie with their ends touching, their concave sides facing so that a narrow lozenge-shaped gap is left between them. This gap or hole is named a stoma.* The two cells which enclose it are called guard cells.

The stomata are minute: about seven ten-thousandths of an inch long and a third as wide (a fine needle makes a hole a hundred times as big). What they lack in size they make up in number: there may be as many as 300,000 in a square inch of leaf surface. A single sunflower leaf may have two million on its lower surface. The lower epidermis is not the continuous film it appears to the eye—it is a perforated sheet, a porous membrane.

The cells of the epidermis are transparent, containing large vacuoles full of water; the thin layer of cytoplasm and the small nucleus can with difficulty be made out in the living cells. The guard cells have thicker walls and contain a few small green bodies. The significance of the form of the guard cells, of the green bodies which they contain, and of the stomata themselves, will appear later.

To penetrate that glistening green mass within the epidermis, the mesophyll, it is necessary to cut thin slices, sections, from the blade.† Almost any slice of the blade will do, providing we avoid

---

* The Greek word for "mouth"; the plural is "stomata."

† To slice such a delicate object by hand into sections thin enough for microscopic study is difficult, though possible. We have recourse to various mechanical methods to obtain unbroken thin slices (as thin as 1/100 millimeter, 1/2500 inch). The leaf may be frozen, and sections cut from the lump of ice which contains it by a machine called a microtome. Or it may be killed with alcohol or some other poison and embedded in paraffin, which plays the same part as ice in holding the soft parts of the leaf in place. After the sections are made, the ice is allowed to melt or the paraffin is dissolved away, leaving the extremely delicate slices adhering to a glass slide. These may then be stained with various aniline dyes to make the different sorts of cells more easily visible, and permanently covered with Canada balsam and a cover-glass. Such preparations will last for years.

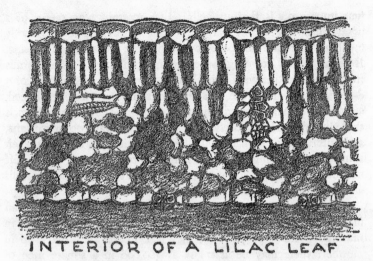

INTERIOR OF A LILAC LEAF

the larger veins; the structure of the blade is uniform throughout. We do not need a complete slice across the leaf; nor could we see such a section in one microscopic view. The fraction of a millimeter which is all we see in the field of vision of a microscope is sufficiently representative of the whole blade.

We can easily identify, in such a section, the epidermis, a single layer of transparent cells above and below. In this view they are not wavy in outline; they are nearly rectangular, except that their upper and lower walls bow out a little. The guard cells are cut across in various directions (since they lie at random in all sorts of positions), and appear in various forms according to the planes in which they are cut. If the knife passes directly across a stoma at its widest point, the guard cells will appear almost round, with the gap, the stoma, between. These will be seen mostly in the lower epidermis; they are rare in the upper. (In vertical leaves, however, such as those of an iris, there are stomata on both sides; and leaves that float on water, such as those of water-lilies, have stomata on the upper side only.)

Just beneath the upper epidermis, hanging from it side by side like a cluster of stalactites, are longish narrow cells fancifully referred to as palisade cells. Sometimes there is just one tier of them, sometimes—in a leaf which has developed in full sunlight—several tiers. These cells are bright green: the color is found in certain small bodies, which float in the protoplasm, and which are to be discussed later. Beneath the palisade in turn, occupying the space between it and the lower epidermis, is a jumble of cells of irregular shapes; cells bulging out here and there, touching each other and the palisade cells only at the projecting parts, and leaving large spaces between. They too are green: the green bodies are perhaps not quite so numerous in them as in the cells above. These cells form an irregular meshwork something like that of a sponge, and are called, in fact, the spongy tissue. The spaces between the cells all communicate; they form a branching system of spaces; and in the living leaf they are filled with something that we have not hitherto encountered in the interior of plants: air. The blade of a leaf is partly air. And this internal atmosphere is joined with the atmosphere of the outer world by those holes in the epidermis already noticed, the stomata.

That is what leaves are: thin layers of brilliantly green cells, rather loosely arranged in the lower half of the thickness of the blade; fitted delicately between two transparent sheets made largely of cellulose; the whole stiffened and held in place by a fine skeleton of veins. Among and around the cells flows air, air like that outside the leaf (except in the relative concentrations of its various gases, as will be seen); air that passes out of the leaf through the stomata into the outside world, to be replaced by new air that enters through the same openings.

THE LEAF WASTES WATER

A canvas bag filled with water and hung up in the air is damp to the touch and water evaporates from its surfaces. (Since evaporation has a cooling action, the water in the bag stays cooler than the air; a fact long known to travelers in deserts.) The inner cells of a leaf resemble the canvas bag in some ways. They are mostly water—large vacuoles surrounded by thin sacs of protoplasm. The cellulose walls offer no barrier to the passage of water; indeed they imbibe water and are normally soaked. Large parts of the surfaces of the cells are exposed to the inner air of the leaf. The water in them, thus in contact with air, acts as water always does under such conditions: it changes from the liquid to the gaseous state, it evaporates. The cells of the epidermis are in contact with the *outer* air; however, their outer walls are covered with a more or less continuous film of a waxy material called cutin, which retards the passage of water to some extent. Loss of water from the epidermal cells is not so great as from the cells of the spongy tissue; it usually amounts to 10 per cent or less of the total loss of a leaf. From the spongy tissue water may evaporate rapidly into the spaces between the cells; and since this gaseous water can move out through the stomata into the world outside, the air inside the leaf does not become saturated and evaporation from the cells continues. The process is known as transpiration: the loss of water from living leaves by evaporation.

Although stomata are very small as compared with a pinprick, they are large in comparison with the particles of water; it would take more than 20,000 molecules of water, side by side, to equal the length of a stoma.

Leaves may lose water also in liquid form. The so-called dewdrops often seen at the points of the teeth of a strawberry leaf are not dewdrops but drops of water exuded by the leaf through certain special cells. This is called guttation (from the Latin *gutta*, a "drop of liquid"). It is not included in transpiration and is less important in the life of the plant.

The amounts of water lost by evaporation from plants are much greater than we generally realize. A full-grown corn plant will transpire a gallon or more a day in normal summer weather: twice its own body weight! To put it differently, during one hour of a hot day more water passes through a leaf than that leaf ever contains at one time. It is as if the leaf were a sort of pump, moving water from the stem out into the air. During the entire growing season it is estimated that a corn plant loses over 50 gallons of water; a field of corn gives off—wastes—enough water to cover the field more than a foot deep. If the field is just an acre—a small cornfield—the plants on it will run up the rather staggering deficit of something like 350,000 gallons of water during their growth.

The amounts vary, of course, not only with the climate and the length of the growing season but with the kind of plant. A potato vine will lose approximately 25 gallons during the season, a tomato plant 35, and a plant of giant ragweed the astonishing total of 140 gallons. Large trees, of course, drink up tremendous quantities of water, casting most of it out upon the summer breezes. It is difficult to count and to measure the leaves of a big maple; but estimates, even if very rough, still serve to emphasize the quantities with which we are dealing. It has been estimated that a silver maple may have 177,000 leaves with a total area of over a million square inches; and there may be more than 100,000 stomata to each square inch! And it has been estimated that such a tree may transpire a maximum of 15 gallons an hour. Perhaps the record is held by a date palm growing in an oasis in the Sahara, its feet in water but its leaves in the hot dry air of the desert. It has been calculated that such a tree may move up through its stem and out through its leaves 100 gallons or more every day. At the other extreme is the thirty-foot columnar cactus growing in our southwestern desert without the benefit of an oasis; losing only a fraction of a quart a day. This is exceptional; conservation of water is practiced by relatively few plants—highly specialized members of the plant kingdom. The great prairies and forests and cultivated lands of the earth are continually giving off water in astronomical amounts, water that rises in an invisible cloud into the air above, and forms visible clouds when it finds a layer of cooler air; water which ultimately descends again as rain, only to be absorbed by yet other plants and to repeat the cycle. I have heard the suggestion that trees were nothing but great weeds, and should be cut down so as to prevent such a waste of water. But it is easy to see that they have a profound effect on the climate of the regions around them, especially of lands to the leeward of them. The water which sweeps across the continent can descend many times as rain and humidify the air many times in its upward escape through the "mouths" of millions of leaves. Unfortunately man, in his efforts towards civilization, has cut down the forests he found to make room for his crops and houses and roads and cities; cut them too ruthlessly, so that the water from the ocean is driven over the dried lands, only to devastate when it does fall.

But though in this way a case may be made for the advantages of transpiration, the continual escape of water creates a serious problem for the plants and for the grower of plants; the most serious of all their problems. Everyone knows that the first requisite of land that is to be planted to crops or to a garden is a supply of water. If it does not descend in sufficient amounts from the heavens, it must be brought in by ditches from a reservoir or pumped from wells. Gardeners must play their hoses almost daily in our unstable eastern climate. In many parts of the western United States it has been found profitable to install sprinkler systems to water pastures and vegetable gardens. If the water supply is very variable, disasters will sometimes occur. Many of us remember the brown fields of the central states, the withered corn-stalks only knee-high in September, after the great drought of 1934, when scarcely any rain fell from March to September. The housewife knows that a drought on a smaller scale will quickly have a similar effect on her house-plants.

Water plays many parts in a plant. Most of what is taken from the earth is lost to the air; but as it rises through the root and through the stem into the leaf, cells along its path make a small levy on it; and this is essential to their life. It creates a pressure within the cells, those delicate and fluid sacs which are mostly water; keeping them distended, pressing against each other so as to form a firm body. If water is lost by the leaves more rapidly than it is supplied by the roots, then all the cells give up some of their water; their pressure, their turgor, is lost; they become flaccid, and the plant wilts, no longer able to spread its leaves to the life-giving sun and air. Water is responsible for the enlargement of new cells, for the invasion of the soil by new root-tips, for the unfurling of the new leaves, for the upthrust of the stems that bear them. Water also enters into the composition of the protoplasm itself; without water no new protoplasm can be formed, no new cells. Water is the solvent in which the minerals and foods of the plants are dissolved, and only in this state can they pass from cell to cell and combine with each other and with other things in all the complex chemistry of life. Water is one of the materials from which sugar is made in leaves (p. 78). The lack of water, therefore, may be detrimental in more than one way. Deficiency of water, a plant physiologist has remarked, is probably the greatest single cause of the death of plants under natural or even cultural conditions.

This continual and dangerous waste of water seems an unexpected and unwarranted result of the beautiful internal structure of a leaf. Why should leaves have stomata, and cells arranged to form a sponge? With the strong tendency to assume that everything that occurs in a living being is caused by a purpose—with this tendency that we have already noticed among those who seek to explain the activities of plants—it has been natural to suppose that there must be something good about transpiration, something which offsets its dangers and explains why it occurs. Surely everything is for the best in this world.

It has been assumed, for instance, that transpiration cools the leaf; for evaporation absorbs heat and thus cools the surfaces from which it occurs. This is evident in the evaporation of sweat from our own skins; also in the desert water-bag already mentioned. Transpiration does cool leaves. But on a hot summer day the reduction in temperature amounts only to 4 or 5 degrees Centigrade (7-9 degrees Fahrenheit); not a critical difference. We cannot imagine that the leaf would come to any harm if this cooling effect were somehow suspended. It has been pointed out that transpiration is responsible for the rapid movement of sap up the stems of plants (for the moving molecules, as they leave the cells of the leaf, tend to exert a pull on the liquid which they are leaving), and that this accelerates the movements of the minerals and other substances carried in the sap. This also is true; these substances do travel more rapidly up the plant when transpiration is rapid. But again the plant would suffer no harm if their movement were less rapid; the cessation of transpiration does not lead to critical shortages of such materials in the upper parts of a plant. As for the movement of the water itself—transpiration certainly has a lot to do with it; but if there were no loss of water from the leaves there would be no need for such a stream of water to pass up the stem.

All in all, it seems safe to say that the plant could do very well without transpiration; that, *as far as the water supply itself is concerned*, it would be better if there were no stomata and no spongy tissue.

There are, in fact, some "safety-devices" built into the leaf, which are very effective under ordinary conditions. The cutin on the epidermis—particularly on the upper epidermis, which is more exposed to the evaporating influence of the sun—is such a factor, of greater or less efficiency. The fact that the stomata are mostly on the lower side protects them from the direct sunlight which would otherwise speed up the movement of water through them. Some leaves are so constructed that they curl up when water is scarce within them—curl up so as to cover the lower surface. But there is something more important and more striking which tends to reduce evaporation in times of danger. The stomata *are not fixed openings*; they change, they open and close automatically. They close at night and at times when the water content of the leaf is low. They thus reduce the passage of gaseous water from the interior to the exterior of the leaf, especially during the night and during periods of drought. Their ability to close depends on peculiarities in the guard cells.

These may have walls which are very thick on their upper and lower sides but thin in the middle; on the side next to the opening, the stoma itself, the two massive walls of each cell, above and below, almost meet. When the guard cell is distended by an abundance of water, the two thick parts are forced apart, much as if

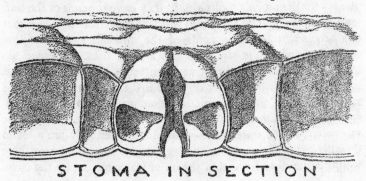

STOMA IN SECTION

they were hinged together. When the cell loses its inner tension—when the supply of water to the cells of the leaf is insufficient to keep them turgid—the thick walls tend to approach each other, the angle between them decreasing; in this condition the guard cell is flatter and broader, and touches or almost touches its sister cell, reducing or closing the opening between them. So by this curious mechanism the rate of transpiration is greatly reduced at times when the water supplies of the cells of the leaf are low. The night-closing depends partly upon the presence of those green bodies already noticed in the guard cells, partly upon conditions in the rest of the leaf.

The great variation in leaves already intimated concerns their water-holding ability. The thick felt of hairs on a mullein leaf may slightly reduce the movement of the air over the surface of the leaf; moving air carries off the evaporated water more rapidly and permits further evaporation. It is perhaps significant, therefore, that such a leaf is commonly found on exposed rocky hillsides and in open fields where temperatures are high and water often scanty; while the delicate smooth leaves of many ferns are usually limited to shady ravines and damp woods, where there is more moisture in the air, less movement of the air, and consequently a lower rate of evaporation. The waxy surface of succulent plants helps to retard the passage of water through epidermal cell walls into dry air. Air spaces are less abundant inside than in ordinary leaves, so that fewer cells are in direct contact with air. Even more effective are certain chemical peculiarities of these leaves; they usually contain organic acids and other substances (very evident in "bitter aloes") which "bind" the water chemically. Some plants have few or no leaves; the cactus already mentioned is leafless, its stem doing the work of leaves but offering, in its more compact structure and smaller surface in proportion to volume, less opportunity for the evaporation of water than would the looser texture and wider expanses of leaves. In short, as we examine plants, either with the naked eye or through a microscope, we cannot but be impressed by the number of special features which are related to the escape of water. In contrast to all such peculiarities of structure, it may be noticed that leaves which grow normally under water lack cutin and are frequently of an extremely simplified structure; *their* problem is with light, not water.

But in spite of all the "devices" which tend to conserve water (and it is a constant temptation to regard them as "devised" by some sort of mind, as resulting from something like superhuman ingenuity), plants do lose water at a rapid and often dangerous rate; they do wilt; they do die from lack of water. Mr. Micawber's celebrated definition of solvency may be modified to apply to plants: if water enters the plant more rapidly than it is being lost, all is well; if the supply of water falls only a little below what is needed to replace the loss through transpiration—the plant is physiologically bankrupt.

Almost all the water that is lost by leaves comes from the earth by way of the root system and the stem with its branches. If all plants were transparent, and if the water within were colored, we should be astonished at the constant and rapid motion which occurs in all the apparently inert stems of plants during their seasons of vigorous life. Recently it has been shown that leaves can also absorb water from the air—water in liquid form, sprayed on them from a hose or from a rain-cloud, or even deposited as dew. This may be used to advantage in the nutrition of our crops.

In a sense, as I have said, the plants which stand everywhere rooted in the earth are so many pumps, through which the waters of the earth are carried up into the atmosphere. Some water is retained by the plants, used in their manufacturing processes, built into their living matter, accumulated in the vacuoles of cells— particularly in underground tubers and succulent fruits. But most of the water which the plant takes up from its surroundings is taken up only to be given off again.

THE STEM REPLENISHES

Once we have seen inside a leaf we can understand how —and why—water escapes from plants. To understand how the supply is replenished necessitates further acquaintance with the anatomy of a plant; in particular with the inner parts of stems and roots.

The stream of sap, the transpiration stream, may move up a stem at the rate of three inches a minute—fifteen feet an hour. But it cannot move from living cell to living cell at this rate or anything near it. That rather viscous material, the protoplasm, which lines the wall of every living cell, impedes the motion; and there are millions of such layers of protoplasm in a few inches of plant body. The water moves, not through living cells, but through long narrow passages, tubes which once were cells but are no longer alive and are now only the walls of cells. These tubes form part of what is known as the vascular or conductive system of a plant.

The vascular system contains other elements besides the passages through which water passes (p. 90); the latter, however, are usually the most conspicuous parts of the system and serve to identify it; they make it visible, in fact, here and there through the plant without any aid from a microscope, for these vessels that carry the sap form much of the rigid skeleton and toughening material of the stem and leaves. They contribute to that network of veins throughout the blade of a leaf, that firm mesh around which the soft green flesh is loosely wrapped. They are found also in the midrib, with which all the veins, directly or indirectly, are connected. And from the midrib they pass down through the leafstalk and into the stem, where they join the main system of waterpipes of the plant. These extend the length of the stem, sending branches into every leaf and every branch, every flower and fruit. They are fed from below by a similar system in the roots, which runs out into every branch of the root system, almost reaching the apical meristems and the regions of elongation.

These water-carrying pipes are of many sizes and shapes, but all share certain peculiarities. They are all long in proportion to their width; and in width some are quite large. They have rather thick walls, which are of cellulose more or less impregnated with a material called lignin, and which are usually decorated with pits, pores, rings, bars, or other thin or thick parts variously arranged. They begin their history as living cells; but when they reach maturity the living protoplasm within the walls dies and disintegrates, leaving a cavity filled with water and various materials dissolved in the water. The lignification of their walls converts the cellulose into what we know as wood; collectively the water-carrying vascular tissues form the wood of the plant, or more technically, the xylem.* There is wood even in herbaceous plants, even in green leaves. We may speak of a carrot or turnip as being woody and therefore unpalatable or inedible; but there is wood even in the tenderest young carrots and turnips, even in spinach and cauliflower. We think of wood as composing the trunks of trees, which furnish the material from which we build houses; but the thin tough strands which help a grass leaf to stand erect are of the same nature—chemically and physically—and receive the same name.

The largest elements of the xylem are the so-called vessels. Each of these was formed from a row of cells, a column or file which extended lengthwise in the stem, root, or vein; the end walls became perforated or entirely disappeared, so that the entire row came to form one long tube. These often reach great lengths—estimated up to ten feet, an astonishing size for one anatomical element of a plant—and may be wide enough to be seen with the unaided eye. They offer the best passage for the flow of water. Somewhat less efficient are narrower ducts, each formed from one elongated cell, narrow and pointed at each end.† Though these also are long, for cells, they are much shorter than the vessels: only about half an inch long at most. Water passing through their narrow lumina must traverse end walls more frequently than in the vessels. There are also long narrow cells with still smaller cavities and thick walls, of little use for conducting water but valuable as parts of the structural framework; these are called fibers. Mixed with all these types of wood elements we may find some living cells, thin-walled and not so greatly elongated.

The arrangement of wood in an herbaceous plant (or in the younger parts of a woody plant) bears a curious and interesting resemblance to the use of structural materials in buildings planned

* The Greek word from which this is derived, and which means "wood," is seen also in "xylophone."

† Vessels are called tracheae (singular trachea); the smaller tubes formed from single cells are tracheids. The Greek word from which these words are derived signifies "rough"; it was first used to describe the windpipe of an animal; early botanists saw some resemblance between this and the water-ducts of plants.

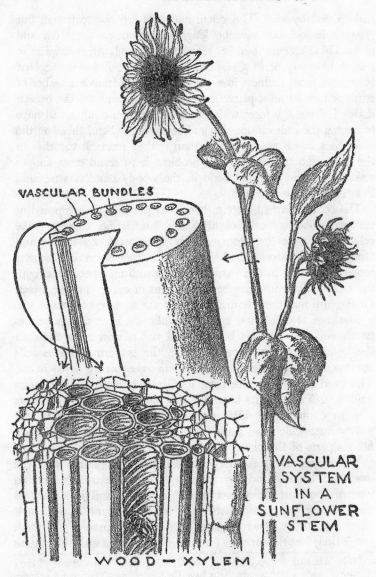

VASCULAR BUNDLES

VASCULAR
SYSTEM
IN A
SUNFLOWER
STEM

WOOD — XYLEM

and erected by man. The xylem elements are not scattered, but grouped in bundles running lengthwise through the stem and roots. These vascular bundles are the long tough strips familiar in a stalk of celery or in a plantain leaf. Every builder knows that to get the most stiffness in a column or pillar from a number of strips or rods he must place them as far as he can from the center; if this is done any force which tends to bend the pillar will have to stretch the rods on one side and compress or bend them on the other to a much greater extent than if they were all together in the center. In the stem, whose problem is to stand erect and to resist forces which would bend it, the woody bundles are found in a ring near the surface.*

The central part of a stem, known as the pith, is composed of thin-walled watery cells of little structural value; these are the cells which were first recognized as living units by Hooke and Grew (p. 28). Later in the life of the stem they often die. Air may replace the water in them and the whole pith may become a light, dry mass which can easily be scraped out or even removed intact. Or the pith may entirely disappear, leaving a central hollow.

The type of cell found in the pith also occupies the spaces between adjacent vascular bundles and the narrow zone between the bundles and the outermost layer, the epidermis. These cells are called by the ancient if rather meaningless name parenchyma. The word actually means, from its Greek derivation, "something poured in." It owes its botanical adoption to the early botanists who were unable to distinguish the cells, and saw only a soft watery mass which had been "poured in" among the more stable, fibrous parts of the plant.

Parenchyma is so abundant in all parts of the plant that the word has become indispensable in the vocabulary of even an amateur botanist. It is everywhere in plants and is largely responsible for the characteristic ways in which plants and animals differ. As will be shown on later pages, though mature they have not entirely lost the capacity for multiplication and growth. In their

---

* The stems of different kinds of plants vary greatly in the details of their structure. Many young woody stems have their xylem in a continuous cylinder near the surface rather than in a discontinuous cylinder of bundles. However, in their essentials a vast number of plants are alike in this respect. The account here given is good for most young herbaceous stems.

large vacuoles there may be quantities of sugar or starch or other accumulated foods; a potato is mostly parenchyma, and so is an apple.

When a young herbaceous stem is cut across it appears (through the microscope) to be built of concentric rings. First, on the outside, is the epidermis, usually a single layer of cells, often with hairs of various types projecting from them; then the narrow outer zone of parenchyma; then the ring of vascular bundles; finally the central pith. Anatomists usually group these parts into three regions: the epidermis, the cortex, and the stele. The cortex is the part which extends from the epidermis approximately to the vascular bundles; the stele includes the vascular bundles and everything within them. The stele is much the largest of the three, and is responsible for the important work of conduction of water,* besides furnishing most of the structural material of the stem. The cortex is of minor importance; but its outer cells, next to the epidermis, often become thick-walled and tough and add to the rigidity of the stem.

In one important group of plants, the monocots, the stem is not so beautifully organized; there is no division into stele and cortex, and the vascular bundles are scattered throughout the stem instead of being arranged in a cylinder. This is evident from even a crude dissection of a corn stem; the long tough strings that pervade the entire stem are the vascular bundles.

When we come to the root, we are dealing with something not usually subjected to forces which would bend it, but to lengthwise pulls from the stem above. In it we find the same sorts of cells, but arranged in a strikingly different way; and, again, arranged in a way that corresponds with the structural principles used in human industry. If the wood of a root were arranged as in a stem, the pulls to which it is subject might easily snap the bundles one by one and the root would no longer anchor the plant safely to the earth. But the wood of the root is concentrated in the center, forming a solid tough core like a rope; just as we use a thin strong cable to anchor a boat, not a group of wires separated from each other by a soft core.

---

* And, as will appear later, of food.

The central core of wood in a root is usually ridged; in cross section it may appear like a star with three, four, or more points. The root is organized in the same three concentric parts as the stem, and the same words are used to name them: epidermis, cortex, stele. But the central part, the stele, is relatively much smaller, and the cortex, composed of parenchyma as in the stem, is relatively enormous. The stele is much more clearly marked than that of a stem. It is bounded by a cylinder of more or less rectangular, thin-walled cells which retain their capacity for division and growth. From some of them arise small masses of cells which become the tips of branch roots. These, as already mentioned, push their way out through the cortex and epidermis.

Again the monocots provide an exceptional sort of structure. They generally have some parenchyma—pith—in the center of their roots; but not nearly so much as there is in a stem.

The same principles of construction are to be found in the venation of leaves, particularly in that of large leaves. It is said

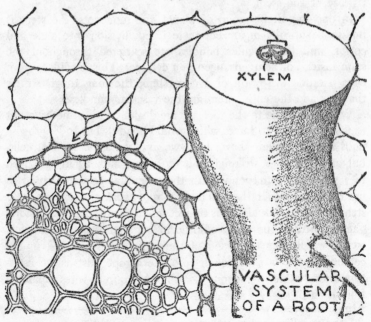

XYLEM

VASCULAR SYSTEM OF A ROOT

that Joseph Paxton derived the idea for the framework of the famous Crystal Palace erected in Hyde Park in 1851 from the veins of the leaves of the giant water-lily of the Amazon, which had been introduced into English hothouses a short time before. The enormous pads of this plant are composed of fragile, thin-walled cells, like those of any leaf. They are easily punctured; yet the Indians who plied those tropical waters for a day's fishing used to place their children on the pads and leave them there—in comparative safety, so long as they sat still. If precautions are taken to distribute the weight evenly, a full-grown man may be supported by one of these leaves. The secret of their strength is to be found in the veins, which form a system of girders projecting from the lower surface and radiating from the place where the blade joins its stalk. The girders stand vertically, just as they do in our buildings, and so offer all their substance in depth to resist bending; they are joined by smaller girders which prevent them from falling sideways, and these in turn are braced by smaller veins which rise from the surface of the blade. This is an exceptional leaf; but the same sort of structure may be found in ordinary leaves, the strengthening veins being in the interior of the blade and projecting only slightly from the surface. The veins owe their rigidity partly to the xylem in them, partly to thick-walled cells which envelop the vascular elements.

THE ROOTS ABSORB

Almost all the water that a plant has in it comes from the soil. The soil, the good earth, is a mass of tiny particles of irregular shapes and various sizes, with spaces between. Some of the particles are mineral—small bits of rock or sand. Some are organic—the remains of dead leaves and stems and roots, or of the parts of dead animals. Some—the most important of all for plants—are of clay; which is mineral matter of a certain kind, in that special condition called colloidal (p. 29). The physics and chemistry of these ingredients and of the complex system which they form are too involved for treatment here. We may, however, easily distinguish several ways in which water is present in the soil. If you dig down deep enough, you will "strike water"; water will stand in the hole you have made. Here is the water table, the surface of what is practically an underground lake or stream mixed with the lower strata of soil. Above this the water is held in the minute spaces between the soil particles and in films around the particles. Different kinds of soil differ in their ability to hold water. Water runs away into sand and is soon lost from the upper levels; in a heavy clay it is held and makes mud. The organic particles which are usually mixed with clay in a good garden loam help to temper both of these undesirable extremes: the water is held in reasonable quantities by capillary forces; but not too much of it.* In any soil, of course, the amount of water will vary from time to time; with the rain which falls upon it and with variations in the water table.

Into this variable and complicated mixture grow the roots which obtain the water which is used—or wasted—by plants in such quantities. If water is abundant, so abundant that it fills every space in the soil, the roots have no problem in reaching and absorbing it; on the other hand, most roots will not thrive in such a setting, for they need air also.† At the other extreme is soil that is, for the purposes of plants, dry. It may have water held in the clay itself, forming a part of the colloidal structure; but this is unavailable, for the forces which bind it to the clay are greater than those which cause water to enter roots. Between these two extremes is ordinary soil with a moderate amount of water; water held in the capillary spaces, the smallest chinks between the soil particles, and surrounding these particles in thin films, but not filling all the interstices. This is the water on which a plant normally depends.

Any cell of the epidermis of the root can take in water; but in tapping the minute reservoirs of water the root-hairs play an important part. They extend out from the surface of the root, between the particles, following their contours and bathed throughout their lengths in the films of water which surround the particles. They increase enormously the surface exposed to water. It has been

* *Capilla* in Latin means "a hair." It has long been known that water will rise in a hair-like—i.e. a very slender—tube; the force which causes such a rise is known as capillarity. Capillarity causes the penetration of water into the minute apertures between the particles of soil.

† Like other parts of plants, they respire; see p. 93.

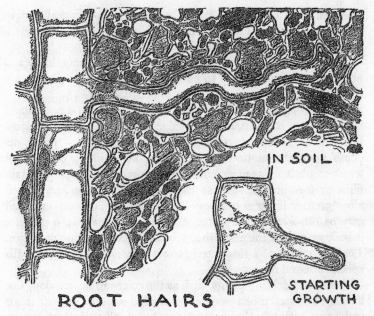

IN SOIL

ROOT HAIRS

STARTING GROWTH

estimated that root-hairs multiply the absorptive surface tenfold or more. A single rye plant has been calculated to have 14 million root-hairs on all its roots!

The importance of the root-hairs is well known to every plant grower—even if he has never heard of them. If a living plant, roots and all, is carefully lifted from the earth, and loose soil gently shaken off, small lumps of soil will be seen to adhere near the ends of the roots, in the regions we have already seen to be covered with root-hairs. Each lump of soil is held by the hairs embedded in it and clinging so intimately to all its minute parts. If the plant is now placed in new soil, water will continue to move in through the root-hairs, which have been undisturbed in the operation. But if the ends of the root are torn off, with their hairs, or if the hairs are stripped off by removing the earth in which they lie, the chances are that the plant will not be able to take in enough water to supply the leaves (even though some of them have been removed); and the result will be failure. I know a suburban couple who carefully removed all the dirt from the roots of a dogwood tree in preparation to installing it in their garden; and subsequently deplored their "bad luck" with plants.

The forces which cause the water to enter the root hairs and other cells of the root and to pass up the stem into the leaves are complex and not even yet wholly understood.

The most important of these processes is osmosis. To understand it necessitates considerable knowledge of physics, and an explanation cannot be here attempted. It must suffice to say that it depends upon the motion of molecules, the ultimate particles of which a substance is made, and upon curious properties of certain films or membranes, such as those of living protoplasm, which afford passage to water but deny it to some of the substances which may be dissolved in the water. As a result of osmosis, a pressure is built up within the cells: they are said to be in a state of turgor. The protoplasm of a turgid cell presses outwards against the walls which surround it.

Young and delicate plants, such as the coleus in my window, not having developed much wood or other rigid material in their stems and leaves, maintain their erect stature largely through the turgor of their cells; one pressing against another so that together they form a firm mass. If I forget to water them, the stems will droop and the leaves hang flaccid from them. If water is supplied before the condition has lasted too long, they will slowly rise again to an erect position, their leaves extended horizontally. If the stalk of a dandelion is split into four quarters from the bottom up but left entire in the upper part, and the whole immersed in water, the four free ends will curl strongly outwards; turgor causes an expansion of the internal cells which have thin and elastic walls, while the thicker-walled epidermal cells cannot enlarge to the same extent. The curling may be reversed by placing the stalk in a solution of salt or sugar, which causes the water to reverse its flow. And this curling and uncurling may be repeated many times.

But osmosis does not completely explain the absorption of water by plants. It is easy to see how water may thus enter cells; but not so easy to understand how they pass it along to the vascular system. There is no doubt that they do so. It has been demonstrated that the cells of a root generate a considerable pressure of water. If the stem of a plant is cut off, the stump may often be seen to ooze water, which is being, as it were, forced up by the roots. The same thing is seen when you prune your grape-vines; it is commonly referred to as "bleeding." There are forces within the root which are responsible for this root pressure, forces not as yet completely identified by botanists.

In many plants root pressure probably helps the sap to rise in the stem. But it is far less important than the force, already mentioned, which is initiated by transpiration from the leaves. Molecules of water passing out from the cells of the leaves into the air create a definite tension in the water left behind; for even water coheres —its molecules have an attraction for one another. Under ordinary conditions with which we are familiar, in lakes and streams and in our household plumbing, this cohesive force is not sufficient to raise a column of water; but in plants the water is supported and held in long strings of microscopic width, each weighing very little, and each free to move. Under these conditions it has been shown that the pull exerted by transpiration is sufficient to move the water up.

There are even those who think that it is enough to pull the water into the root from the soil; they speak of an "active" absorption of water by the plant in contrast to (or in addition to) the "passive" process in which the motive power is contributed by the water itself, by the motion of its restless molecules. This subject is still, as I write, controversial, and we can draw no sure conclusions.

Whatever be the mechanism involved, whether active or passive, it is certainly true that water passes into the root-hairs rather rapidly; rapidly enough to create a zone, a cylinder of relatively dry soil around each root. After this has happened, how can the plant continue to obtain water? Must it wait until the dry soil has replenished itself from the water table, or until rain falls and saturates the soil? Instead of waiting, the root grows continuously. The root-hairs in the dried-out zone wither, the epidermis itself is lost, the absorption of water ceases in that particular part; in fact cells beneath the epidermis may become corky and impervious to water (see p. 106); but meanwhile a new region of root-hairs has appeared, formed of new cells which have just accomplished their elongation; and this taps a new cylinder of soil. We may picture the earth beneath and around a plant as filled with tiny root-tips, elongating, questing, thrusting themselves into new parts of the soil and tapping the water there held by means of their newly formed root-hairs. The earth from which the plant is taking its water is farther and farther from the point at which the seed germinated. Nurserymen recognize this when they prune off the longer roots; this stimulates the appearance of new roots nearer to the crown of the plant and keeps the absorptive zone within a manageable "ball" of earth.

4

The Food of Plants

FOOD COMES FROM LEAVES

Is a leaf then of no use to a plant? Is it merely a means of losing water, to the imminent peril of life? Would a plant be better off without its leaves? Such absurd questions serve to emphasize the fact, now generally known but quite unsuspected by the fathers of botany, that green leaves provide the food of the plant; and not only of that plant but also of other plants that have no green leaves of their own and no green color at all; and not only of these but also of animals, including ourselves.

There is no essential difference between plant food and animal food. We are sometimes confused by the common habit of speaking of (and marketing) fertilizer as "plant food"—the fertilizer which we add to the soil of our gardens. But this, while it does nourish the plant, and is essential to its growth,* is not *food* in the same sense as the food which we ourselves need: we cannot support ourselves, even if we wish to, on the unpalatable stuff that we buy for our plants. Neither is it *food* for them; they use the same kinds of food, and in the same way, as we do ourselves—being alive, as we are. The word food, as the biologist uses it, and as it is used in this book, refers to the materials which we use daily under that name: sugar, starch, fats, oils, proteins, and so forth. These are used by plants also.

A moment's reflection shows that there *is* food in plants—food in the above sense. We value apples and pears and oranges and

---

* In ways to be made plain below; see p. 81.

bananas for their sugar. Our chief source of starch is the grains of domesticated grasses—wheat, oats, barley, rice, and the rest. We obtain oil from olives and peanuts and coconuts and cottonseed and flaxseed. *All these foods are traceable to the green leaves of plants.* And even the fats and proteins of our meats have the same origin—the leaves upon which the animals grazed. *All the food of the world begins its career in the green parts of plants*—mostly in leaves.

Notice the word green which recurs so frequently in the preceding paragraphs. It may seem strange that a color, a pigment, is worth mentioning in connection with the food supply of the world; but this color is of vital importance in the production of food. As has been previously pointed out, the color is not on the surface of the leaf; nor is it on the surface of the cells within the leaf. It is not dissolved in the fluids of the cells; the cells are not uniformly green throughout, as they would be if this were true. The green pigment is contained in small bodies which form part of the protoplasm of the cells of the mesophyll (p. 51). These bodies are called chloroplasts; and the green material which they carry is chlorophyll.*

These minute green bodies are in that part of the protoplasm which is not nucleus: the cytoplasm. Each is shaped more or less like a round cookie—flattish, nearly circular in outline, thicker in the middle than at the edges. They are rather smaller than the nucleus. Although they have no motion of their own, they may be carried along in the streaming of the mobile cytoplasm, jostling one another and the nucleus in their endless procession around the cell, just inside the walls.

The chlorophyll—it has been called the most important substance in nature—is held in the minute grains within the chloroplasts. It does not dissolve in water. Even if you boil a leaf in water the green color does not come out (except a little from

---

* *Chloro-* in Greek means "green"; *plast*, as in "protoplasm," means "that which forms"; "chloroplast" is the "green-former." The second component of the word "chlorophyll" has already been met with in "mesophyll"; it means "leaf." "Chlorophyll" means "leaf-green."

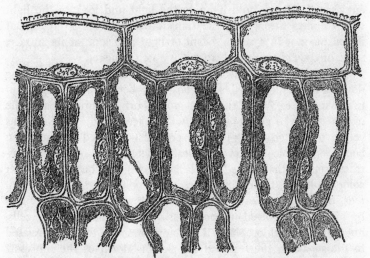

THE FOOD MAKERS
CHLOROPLASTS IN THE PALISADE

broken cells).* But soak it in alcohol or acetone (preferably having first killed it with boiling water), and you will quickly obtain a beautiful dark green liquid. In this are the several pigments which make up chlorophyll, somewhat altered chemically. For we use the word chlorophyll rather loosely. As it exists in the leaf the green stuff is really a mixture of four substances: chlorophyll a, chlorophyll b (both green, the former of a bluer green than the latter), xanthophyll, and carotene (these yellow or orange, becoming visible when the leaves change color in autumn). The two green pigments, the chlorophylls proper, seem to be the ones directly concerned with food-making; we may, therefore, continue to use the word chlorophyll for the mixture.

This green material has a curious property known as fluorescence; which means that it has two different colors in its differ-

---

* Likewise enough chlorophyll will ooze out of crushed cells of grass-blades to leave a smear of green on a white garment.

There are certain other green pigments in some kinds of leaves, which do dissolve out in water; they are distinct from chlorophyll and of no importance in the production of food.

ent aspects. If you hold it up to the light and look at the light which comes through it, the transmitted light, it is green; but if you place it in a strong beam of light and look at its surface, some of the light reflected from it is a rich wine-red.

Chlorophyll is an unstable material—it is constantly breaking down. Fresh chlorophyll is as constantly being manufactured, in the living leaf. When the days grow short in autumn, and the nights cold, the chlorophyll is not replaced, and the leaf turns yellow or orange (the pigments previously masked by the green becoming visible). Likewise a leaf afflicted with nutritional diseases (such as that caused by a lack of iron) may be yellow. Other colors in leaves, the decorative reds of a coleus leaf, the beautiful reds, oranges, bronzes of the annual autumn display, are caused by pigments dissolved in the water of the vacuoles of the cells, not held in the chloroplasts. Their appearance in the fall is related to the sugars in the leaf and the slowing down of the transport of these sugars. But this is getting ahead of our story—the manufacture of food in leaves.

For the green color, the chlorophyll, is connected with the manufacture of food. The first food easily recognized in living green cells is one of the sugars, named glucose*; in most kinds of leaves it is quickly converted into starch. Now it is well known that if starch, which is colorless (it comes on the market usually as a white powder), is treated with a solution of iodine, which is brown, the result is a new color—usually a beautiful dark blue; the two substances, joining together chemically, form a new substance which has the color of neither. So intense is the color even when a very minute amount of starch is present that materials of unknown composition can be tested for the presence of starch by adding a little iodine solution.† Now if a green leaf is removed from a healthy plant which has been standing in bright light at ordinary temperatures; if this leaf is killed by boiling it in

---

* To those who have not studied organic chemistry, it is necessary to point out that "sugar" is not one substance but a class of substances; there are many sugars. The sugar on your table is sucrose.

† Or, of course, tested for the presence of iodine by adding a little starch; but this test is less frequently useful.

water and bleached by extracting the chlorophyll with alcohol; if this leaf is then covered with a solution of iodine, it will turn the characteristic color which shows that it contains starch. But if you run the same test on a leaf which has white stripes in it (such as that of the wandering Jew) or a white margin (as in varieties of geranium and coleus), the blue color will appear only where the green color was present; the white areas make no starch—though microscopic examination shows them to be perfectly normal except for the lack of chlorophyll. *Only living cells which contain chlorophyll* can make starch from the raw materials available in leaves. Furthermore, the leaf must be illuminated. The light strikes down through the transparent upper epidermis into the palisade cells and passes through them lengthwise—with a minimum of obstruction from cell walls; and streams on, with reduced intensity, into the spongy tissue. The chloroplasts—which are particularly abundant in the palisade—are bathed in light, whether direct sunlight or diffused light. And light is energy: it runs the machine, the food-making process. It is easy to show that it is essential to the manufacture of food. If you fasten to the leaf a small device which will cut off the light from a portion of its surface, in a pattern which you can recognize afterwards, and take care that the device has no other detrimental effect on the life of the leaf (such as interference with its supply of air); if you then test the leaf with iodine in the way described above; only the pattern exposed to light will change color. The pattern in the screen is printed on the leaf, as an image is printed on photographic paper. The manufacture of food in leaves *occurs only in illuminated cells*.

The leaves *make* the starch. It is usually not present in them at dawn, and it appears in them only if they contain chlorophyll and are exposed to light. The starch is made from glucose; what is the glucose made from? Like all chemical substances, glucose and starch consist of molecules; a molecule is the unit—a single particle —of a substance, the smallest unit in which that substance can exist. The molecules are made of atoms; some of only one kind of atom, others of several kinds, in various more or less fixed proportions. There are over ninety kinds of atoms known (many of them being quite uncommon). A molecule of the gas oxygen in the free state

—as it exists in air—consists of two oxygen atoms. A molecule of glucose, however, consists of 24 atoms: 6 of carbon, 12 of hydrogen, 6 of oxygen; all joined together in a complex pattern. Chemically it may be written thus:

$$C_6H_{12}O_6$$

Starch has an even larger molecule. It is composed of the same three kinds of atoms, and in nearly the same proportions, but in much greater numbers. There are many varieties of starch, differing in the total number of atoms in their molecules; they may be all represented by the formula:

$$(C_6H_{10}O_5)_n$$

in which the letter n stands for a variable number. The close relationship of these two foods can be seen at a glance; it is not hard to understand that one may be transformed into the other.

The materials from which glucose is made are substances which contain these same atoms; carbon, hydrogen, and oxygen. They are also substances normally present in leaves. They are water and carbon dioxide. The former needs no introduction; it is abundant in every living cell. Carbon dioxide is a gas, everywhere present in the air in minute quantities; and present also, dissolved, in water which is exposed to air, including the water of living cells in the interior of leaves.

These two relatively simple compounds are written chemically H_2O and CO_2. When 6 molecules of water are available, and the same number of molecules of carbon dioxide, their atoms become combined in the new and much more complex molecule of glucose. The following symbolic representation of this event is what is known as a chemical equation:

$$6\,H_2O + 6\,CO_2 \longrightarrow C_6H_{12}O_6 + 6\,O_2$$

It will be noticed that no atoms are lost, nor are any gained in the process; we have the same number of the same kinds of atoms at the end as we had in the beginning. Notice also that oxygen appears in the process, as well as glucose.

The oxygen becomes sufficiently concentrated in the cell that it will escape in gaseous form into the air around the cell—following the same path as the water lost in transpiration. At the same time carbon dioxide is used up in the process, and more will enter the cell from the air, following the usual course of diffusion, and changing from the gaseous to the dissolved state as it does so. It enters the moist cell walls of the mesophyll from the air within the leaf, and more passes in through the stomata to make up for its disappearance.

Now it is plain why a leaf sealed against the loss of water would not make for a successful plant; for the leaf would be sealed also against the entrance of carbon dioxide, and the plant would starve for the lack of one of the ingredients from which it makes its food. Transpiration has been called a "necessary evil"; although it is a wasteful (even a dangerous) process, it must occur, because no land plant could be devised which would retain all its water and at the same time allow the entrance of carbon dioxide.

One thing has been omitted from the chemical picture presented above. The reaction, symbolized by letters, numbers, "plus" signs, and an arrow, is one of those that require the application of energy; just as the motion of water upwards against gravity requires an input of energy. The energy which causes the food to be made is light; and no other kind of energy will do. At least we have not yet discovered how to cause the appearance of glucose (or starch) and oxygen in living cells by applying such forms of energy as heat or electricity. Sunlight is generally the best (either direct or indirect); artificial light can be used, if it is sufficiently intense. Because of the necessity of light, the process is known as photosynthesis: manufacture by light.

What part is played by the chlorophyll? In some way that is still not clear to botanists it absorbs the light and converts it to the sort of energy which will force the atoms of carbon, hydrogen, and oxygen together in the new combination. It is known that chlorophyll absorbs certain colors of light, letting others pass through (that is what makes it look green); it absorbs principally red, blue, and violet. Chloroplasts are extraordinarily numerous—a quarter of a billion beneath each square inch of the surface of an elm leaf, for example. An elm tree has a leaf surface estimated to be nearly an acre; and the chloroplasts in its leaves have a combined surface of some fifteen acres. This is the surface of green-bearing matter exposed to light and to the materials of photosynthesis. With this apparatus a leaf succeeds in making about the thirtieth part of an ounce (one gram) of glucose per square yard per hour. It seems a small amount; but put the figure against the total leaf area of the plant and multiply by the total number of hours of light in the growing season—and it mounts up.

The process does not occur as pictured above; it is not so simple. The absorption of energy involves certain complex compounds containing phosphorus. The first step seems to be the separation of the oxygen from the hydrogen of the water molecules, leaving the hydrogen available for new combinations. At the time in which I write, research into the chemistry and physics of photosynthesis is going on at an increased rate and with increasing success. Part of this accelerated progress may be ascribed to experiments made with chloroplasts removed from living cells and kept active in artificial solutions. Photosynthesis has been studied also in masses of minute aquatic plants, of the kinds that often tinge with green the waters of lakes and ponds. It may be that it will eventually be possible for the chemist to duplicate the entire process in his flasks and test-tubes without the use of living cells; but that time is not yet. And meanwhile, although some of the steps are still hidden from us, the simple equation given above does represent the kinds and numbers of molecules present at the beginning and at the end of photosynthesis.

This is the process upon which the life of all the world depends: the manufacture of glucose (or a similar substance) from water and carbon dioxide in living cells which contain chlorophyll and are exposed to light. This is the process which occurs only in the green parts of plants. This is the source of supply for the carbohydrates from which, as will be seen, are made all other foods and all parts of all living cells. This is the reason why we cultivate gardens and plant crops; and raise animals which consume our pastures and hayfields.

WHY USE FERTILIZER?

If all the foregoing is true, why need we apply fertilizer to the soil of our gardens, manure to our fields? If the plant makes its food from water and air, supplied at no cost to us, of what use is it to add nitrates and phosphates and ill-smelling mixtures in general to our earth?

The reason is plain if we recall the chemical formula of glucose and notice that this sugar—like all sugars, and starches also—contains only three kinds of atoms: carbon, hydrogen, oxygen. These are the most abundant elements in the bodies of plants and animals; but they are not the only ones. A molecule of chlorophyll contains magnesium; and without this atom there can be no chlorophyll. The material which cements cells together is made partly of calcium. Protoplasm itself contains, in addition to carbon, hydrogen, and oxygen, the elements nitrogen and (especially in the nucleus) phosphorus; and plant protoplasm always contains sulphur. In short, there are a number of chemical elements, besides carbon, hydrogen, and oxygen, used by plants in the construction of their bodies as they grow and in the ordinary wear and tear of life—the great complex of activities which the scientist knows as metabolism. These additional elements, not found in the sugar and starch produced by photosynthesis, come from the soil, dissolved in the water which enters the roots. It is this material that must be replenished when successive generations of plants are grown in the same patch of earth.

For many years botanists have taught that ten chemical elements must be present for the normal life and growth of a plant. They are:

carbon (C), hydrogen (H), and oxygen (O), which constitute the basic food, glucose;

nitrogen (N), which is an essential part of every molecule of protein—and protoplasm contains proteins;

sulphur (S), which is a part of the proteins of plants;

phosphorus (P), found in the proteins of the nucleus, and in certain fatty compounds which are essential to the life of every cell;

magnesium (Mg), which is included in the chlorophyll molecule
   and without which new chlorophyll cannot be made;
iron (Fe), which is also necessary to the formation of chlorophyll, though it is not incorporated in the finished product;
calcium (Ca), used in the formation of pectic compounds which
   join cell to cell, and which also takes part in the process by
   which cells divide to form new cells;
potassium (K), whose uses are still obscure, but which is none
   the less known to be necessary.

Carbon and oxygen are obtained by the plant from the air, as
has been set forth in earlier pages. Hydrogen is a part of the water
which enters the soil; additional oxygen is also obtained from this
substance. *And all the others enter the plant through the roots,
dissolved in water.* They are not found in the soil as simple elements, but as compounds—several kinds of atoms joined in one
molecule. Potassium acid phosphate, for instance, consists of
atoms of potassium, of phosphorus, of hydrogen, and of oxygen;
its molecule may be pictured by the expression KH_2PO_4. Calcium
nitrate similarly contains calcium, nitrogen, and oxygen
$[Ca(NO_3)_2]$. Magnesium sulphate ($MgSO_4$) supplies the plant
with magnesium and sulphur. Such compounds are called salts.
If we mix these salts in appropriate proportions and add a small
quantity of, say, iron tartrate, we have made a complete fertilizer
—all the seven elements which a plant gets from the soil are there.
If one of them is omitted (and if it is lacking in the soil), the
plant will be abnormal in some respect: it will have yellow or
bronze leaves instead of green, or the leaves will be malformed, or
the plant will be stunted in its growth, or some other symptom
will appear; and ultimately, if the condition is not remedied, the
plant will die. The lack of nitrogen quickly results in marked
stunting. The absence of iron or magnesium is particularly striking,
for plants deprived of these elements have no chlorophyll.

These salts usually enter the plant from the soil dissolved in the
water there present. We add fertilizer usually in a dry state; the
salts dissolve gradually in the water of the soil and thus become
available to the roots. Recently the use of more soluble fertilizers
has been advocated—salts which will dissolve more easily and more

quickly; and fertilizers to be applied in liquid form, the salts already dissolved, have been recommended. The most startling new aspect of this branch of horticulture is the discovery that liquid fertilizer may be sprayed on the leaves and be absorbed through the epidermis. Scientists have availed themselves of an interesting trick to confirm this. They have used salts containing an atom that is "labeled" by its radioactivity (an offshoot of atomic research) and whose presence can be detected with a Geiger counter; the passage of such an atom from the surface of a leaf into the interior parts and down the vascular bundles into the stem can be followed almost as if we could see it. The absorption by leaves of phosphorus, of magnesium, and of potassium has been demonstrated in this way.

Salts, whether taken from soil or from a spray, are used only in small quantities. In making up solutions in which they grow plants for experimental purposes, botanists commonly add the phosphate at the rate of only about a fiftieth of an ounce to a gallon of water. More nitrate is required than this; but only a fifth of an ounce. And the amount of iron needed is a few thousandths of an ounce. As every grower knows, commercial fertilizers must be used with care; if applied too thickly they will "burn" the plants. That is, when they dissolve in water, the high concentrations will cause the plant cells to *lose* water and eventually to die and become discolored (as if by burning). Even greater care must be used with the liquid fertilizers. In fact the amounts of nutrient salts needed are so small that in parts of this country ordinary tap water contains enough of them to act as a fairly efficient culture solution!

Only in recent years has it been discovered that such a mixture of salts as that described above is, after all, *not* a complete fertilizer. Several other elements are needed by plants for continued health and life; but in such extremely small quantities that the amounts present as impurities in ordinary chemical materials suffice, and so the need for them was not at first detected. There are at least five of these so-called "trace" elements (because only a trace is needed), or micronutrients: boron (Bo), molybdenum (Mo), zinc (Zn), manganese (Mn), copper (Cu). Quite recently it has been demonstrated that chlorine (Cl), which is present in all plants, is necessary at least for tomato plants; it has long been suspected of being one of the essential elements. The rare element vanadium (V) has been shown to be required by one of the microscopic aquatic plants; and selenium (Se) by some of the vetches. It is probable that further discoveries of this kind will be made; such facts were unknown a few years ago because the technique of the older investigators was inadequate for the ultimate purification of the salts which they used. It has been shown that zinc can even dissolve out of the walls of glass vessels in very minute quantities —but quantities sufficient for the uses of plants growing in those vessels.* It has been calculated that the amount of vanadium needed for the small plants mentioned above is the incredibly small quantity of 3,000 atoms per cell.†

Other elements are almost universally present in plants—sodium, aluminum, silicon; some of them are probably useful and may be essential. Iodine is accumulated by some plants; although it is necessary for *our* health, it is not, apparently, for that of the plants. It is becoming clear also that what is necessary for one kind of plant is not always so for another; and that under certain conditions one micronutrient element may be substituted for another.

We do not know just how plants use the micronutrients; we know only that in their absence abnormalities quickly develop. We do not usually bother to add them to our fertilizers; there will be enough in ordinary soil or as impurities in the materials used in compounding the fertilizer. There are soils, however, that are markedly deficient in one or more of the trace elements, and special pains must be taken to correct the condition. It has been reported, for instance, that about 80 per cent of the soils of South Africa are deficient: zinc is lacking in land used for citrus orchards; sulphur in tea plantations; magnesium in banana plantations. In applying micronutrients one must exercise great care not to add

---

* Advance in our knowledge of the part played by vitamins in the life of cells came about in much the same way.

† That this number is really very small is seen by comparing it with Avogadro's number, which is the number of molecules in a milliliter of a gas under standard conditions: it is approximately 2.7×10^{19} (27 quintillions); a milliliter is about the thirtieth part of a fluid ounce.

too much; for, interestingly enough, most of them are poisonous to plants if present in any great concentration. Salts of copper, for instance, are commonly used to kill the unwanted aquatic plants that may choke our ponds and lakes. One can have too much of a good thing!

Aside from these occasionally troublesome but usually ignored elements, it is well known that soils differ greatly in their fertility, in their ability to supply the elements needed in comparatively large quantities. Some soils have, when first planted, everything necessary for a bumper crop; others will scarcely grow anything but unlovely weeds. But there is another and more important reason for adding fertilizers to soils—even to soils well endowed by nature. In uncultivated places a plant—be it a grass or a forest tree—takes up the essential materials from the soil, rich or poor as the case may be, and uses them in its growth; and, when it dies, *returns these materials* to the soil from which it got them, in the ordinary processes of dissolution. The soil is not impoverished; the nutrient elements pass through a history, a cycle, that may be indefinitely repeated. The principal enemies of the system are two: fire and man. When plants—dead or alive—are consumed by fire, the chemical elements in their bodies are reduced to ash; this *may* return to the soil and be available to new vegetation; but it may also blow away or be washed down into the sea, leaving the earth the poorer. Man intensifies the loss in many ways. He does not permit his own substance to return to the soil; and most of what he takes from the earth he *removes from that place*, permanently. The farmer sells his crop; the gardener burns his leaves; everyone burns paper and tobacco; enormous quantities of waste are dumped into the sea. In fact our cities, seen in this light, are nothing but giant funnels through which the natural resources of our land are poured out and lost. A few cities are sufficiently responsible to convert their garbage to a form which can be restored to the fields.

In many ways nitrogen is a crucial element. Plants take up the salts of the earth, including nitrates and nitrites. They use the nitrogen in them, with the atoms of carbohydrates and phosphorus and sulphur, to form proteins. The proteins may come to form part of the protoplasm, the living matter itself. Animals, which feed on plants (directly or indirectly), use the plant proteins to build their own protoplasm. But both plants and animals ultimately die and disintegrate*; the protoplasm is broken down into various substances, among which ammonia is often found; this contains the nitrogen. Minute organisms of the soil called nitrifying organisms convert ammonia into nitrites and nitrates; and we have returned to our starting point. But when plants are burned, the nitrogen is usually lost in the gases formed. The same thing happens when explosives such as dynamite and gunpowder are discharged. Even more insidious are certain microscopic plants in the soil which convert salts of nitrogen into free, gaseous nitrogen (N_2) which escapes from the cycle and is lost to plants. As a partial compensation for these losses, there exist also certain nitrogen-fixing bacteria, which *can* use the free nitrogen of the air and from it form compounds useful to plants—thus returning nitrogen to the cycle again. Some of the nitrogen-fixers live in soil; the best known are those which invade the roots of legumes (peas, beans, vetch, etc.), forming little swellings in which they multiply and carry on their beneficial work, receiving in return protection and nutrition from the host plant.† This is the principal reason for the planting of such crops in poor soils (it is often necessary, when you plant them, to plant the bacteria also, obtaining packages of them from an agricultural experiment station). When a dishonest contractor came by stealth and scraped the topsoil from my piece of land, I planted rye and vetch; and, when I had a good stand, dug it into the subsoil, enriching it with humus (the remains of the plants) and salts of various elements including nitrogen.

Botanists have experimented for many years with plants grown in nutrient solutions of more or less known composition. Only recently (comparatively speaking) did it occur to some growers that such methods might be applied commercially. It is perfectly

---

* Some idea of the processes of disintegration is to be found on p. 222.

† The relationship is an example of what is called symbiosis, from two Greek words meaning "living together"; both participants benefit. If the invading organism is benefited but the host injured, the former is spoken of as a parasite.

feasible to grow plants in sand or in tanks containing nutrient solutions—water in which are dissolved all the essential elements in suitable concentrations. Large crops may thus be obtained in a small space and in a heated glass-house, in despite of frosts; this is the new art of hydroponics, or "soilless agriculture." It has many advantages, especially where population is concentrated, land too valuable for farming of the ordinary kind, and the growing season restricted. But the technique is difficult and the amateur unskilled in chemical procedures may easily be disappointed in his results. Concentrations must be carefully adjusted and maintained at proper levels; air must be introduced for the proper growth of the roots; wastes must be removed. And it must never be forgotten that the amount of growth is limited not only by these nutrients but by the foods—the real foods, traceable to photosynthesis; without these the nutrients from soil or solution are of no use. And foods in turn are limited in quantity by the amount of light available. The short and often dark days of winter and the presence of smoke and fog will interfere with the supply of food, no matter what nutrient materials are supplied to the roots. Artificial light may be used to supplement daylight; but to obtain any useful intensity may be expensive.

Think, then, the next time you rake a pile of leaves into the street to burn them, what you are doing; and withhold the match. All this dead plant substance contains the nutrient elements that came from your garden earth; and back to that earth they should go, as "compost" or "mulch." Otherwise you must buy more fertilizer to replace them, fertilizer which can be traced back to some other patch of earth somewhere, and impoverishes it. The resources of the earth are a precious heritage; a rational human society will make every effort to conserve them.

MOVEMENT OF FOOD THROUGH A PLANT

You will recall that if you pluck a leaf from a healthy plant that has been standing in bright light and subject it to a certain routine, you will find that it contains starch. But if you take another leaf from the same plant *early next morning*, you will find no starch. During the night starch disappears from leaves.*

How is this possible? Solid grains of starch will not dissolve in water (even if they are boiled in water, they do not make a true solution, but a colloidal dispersion). How can these grains leave the cells in which they are made? There are no openings in the walls, nor in the protoplasmic membranes, large enough to allow their passage.

What happens is a very fundamental and important change, familiar to us in our own bodies: digestion. The starch is digested; which means that its molecules are broken into smaller and simpler molecules which *can* dissolve in water. The molecules formed are simply those of our old acquaintance glucose. The starch was formed from glucose, and to glucose it returns. A molecule of starch is essentially made from a number of molecules of glucose, slightly modified and joined together. Digestion is the reverse of this synthesis: from a molecule of starch a number of molecules of glucose are obtained.†

The importance, the necessity of digestion is obvious. Since only green cells exposed to light can manufacture food from the raw materials, all other cells of the plant are dependent upon these manufacturing cells: all the cells of the roots, which are underground and receive no light; most of the cells of stems; and the parts of flowers and fruits which contain no chlorophyll. Food must be supplied to these parts by the leaves; the food must move from cell to cell through the cell walls and through the layers of protoplasm. It is a principle which should be kept constantly in mind in seeking to understand the life of a plant: *only materials dissolved in water can enter or leave living plant cells*. There is no way for solids to pass through their walls and membranes. Even gases, as we have seen, pass in and out of cells dissolved in water. Life goes on in a liquid medium: in water.

---

* This, incidentally, is part of the proof that the starch in a leaf is *made* there; it is not there early in the day, but it is there later.

† When glucose is made into starch, several molecules of water are also formed; the process is known as condensation. When the reverse change—digestion—occurs, water is taken into the molecules; the chemist describes the process as hydrolysis—a loosing or dissolving by means of water.

If it were not for digestion the starch formed in photosynthesis would accumulate indefinitely in the cells in which it is made; it could never leave them; and the rest of the plant—and the whole animal world—would starve.

Some kinds of plants do not change the glucose, the first product of photosynthesis, to starch; for instance, onions. Their leaves are rich in sugar but lack starch. In such plants digestion is not necessary for the movement of the carbohydrate made in the leaves; but it is none the less essential at other points in the life processes.

Digestion has been met with already in these pages: in the germination of seeds (p. 15). The starch in the endosperm of a corn grain is changed to sugar which is used by the embryo. If digestion did not occur the embryo, though almost surrounded by food, would die for lack of food. Even to move starch from the cotyledons of a bean, for example, to the growing tips of root and stem is impossible. The starch must be changed to sugar; the sugar must dissolve in water; then the food can make the necessary journey from cell to cell through the young plant.

Similar things are true of our own bodies. The starch which we take into our mouths—in bread or potatoes—is not yet in our cells; even when it reaches our stomach and intestines the same is true; we have surrounded it, but so long as it remains starch it will be outside our living cells.

How is digestion brought about? Starch may be "digested" for industrial purposes by heating it with sulphuric acid. Obviously this is not what happens within living cells. The protoplasm does it with an enzyme. Enzymes, of which there are many kinds, are concerned in many (if not all) of the chemical changes in cells; and some of them have the remarkable power of causing insoluble starch to change into soluble glucose. The commonest such enzyme is called diastase.

Diastase is formed by the cotyledon of a grain of corn or barley, and passes out into the endosperm; here it brings about the change of the starch into sugar, which moves into the growing embryo. (Germinating barley seeds are a commercial source of this enzyme.) Similarly in our mouths, in our saliva, there is an enzyme very like diastase; we mix the starch thoroughly with the enzyme when we chew our food, and so bring about its conversion into sugar; and the sugar is absorbed through the walls of the intestines into the blood and finally into the cells of the body. Diastase is formed in the cells of the mesophyll at night and works upon the grains of starch formed during the day, causing them to break up into sugar, which dissolves in the water of the cell.

The enzymes resemble what the chemist calls catalysts: substances which accelerate chemical changes without themselves being used up in the process or forming part of the final products. (Catalysts are of great importance in industrial chemistry.) Enzymes are needed only in very small quantities. They are mostly highly specific; that is, one kind of enzyme will affect only one sort of chemical change. Diastase will cause the digestion of starch to sugar but is of no use in the digestion of fat. None of the digestive enzymes has any effect on the synthesis of foods; these and other chemical processes of living cells are dependent upon still other enzymes.

Where does the food move in a plant? Dissolved foods can move from cell to cell, presumably by osmosis. But they actually pass up and down the plant at a more rapid rate through certain special ducts (just as the sap rises through special conductive elements). The parts most responsible for the flow of food are extraordinary cells called sieve elements because their walls are perforated in certain areas by small holes, so that these areas resemble sieves. Through the holes of the sieve the protoplasm passes from one cell to the next. The sieve elements are narrow, elongated, thin-walled; unlike the water-carrying elements of the wood, they are filled with protoplasm; but they are among the very few kinds of living cells known to the botanist which have no nuclei. How do they live without nuclei, which have been shown to be essential to the life of other cells? A complete answer is not yet possible; but each sieve element is associated with a still narrower living cell which *has* a nucleus, a rather large and seemingly active nucleus, which may suffice for both cells (this cell is known as a companion cell). In most flowering plants a series of sieve elements is arranged to form what is known as a sieve tube: a long tube interrupted by partitions perforated by holes.

Sieve tubes, with their companion cells and a few other kinds mixed with them, form what is called the phloem; and this is usually found alongside the wood, the xylem, in leaves, stems, and roots. The vascular structures already noticed* consist not only of xylem but of phloem also. They form passages not only for the rising stream of sap but also for the flow of dissolved food—which may be moving down into the roots, up into the opening buds, out into flowers and fruits—wherever food is being used or accumulated. In a stem the phloem strands lie commonly to the outside of the xylem strands—that is, on the side towards the epidermis. In the veins of a leaf they are beneath the xylem. In a root they are usually of the same number as the ridges on the central core of xylem and alternate with them. The phloem may contain fibers as well as sieve tubes and companion cells; also small parenchyma cells. Phloem is still sometimes referred to by its old name "bast."

Just what causes the food to move through the sieve tubes we do not know. One theory is that it moves rapidly in a mass (rather than slowly by diffusion). The passage of food into growing fruits has been calculated at rates as high as several inches an hour. It is probable that a highly unusual—in fact unique—state of affairs prevails at the sieve plates, which facilitates the rapid passage of food through the openings; but we do not yet know what happens, what forces are involved.

OF WHAT USE IS FOOD?

Return for a moment, if you please, to a point made some pages previously. A distinction was there made between *food*, in the sense of the biologist, and other materials, such as those provided by fertilizers. Food, it was said, is the same for plants and animals; it is what we ourselves need to sustain life; it is sugar and starch and fat and protein and the like and not such things as nitrates and phosphates.

---

* Pp. 61, 62; and the drawings on pp. 63, 66.

But, it may be said, are not *all* these things, the elements of the soil as well as the products of photosynthesis, necessary to life? Are they not *all* used in the construction of the plant, in the formation of its framework, its protoplasm, its pigments, its reservoirs of food? Is not the magnesium obtained from the commercial fertilizer just as important in forming a new molecule of chlorophyll as the glucose obtained from photosynthesis? Why should any such distinction be made between two kinds of materials, both necessary, both nutritious? Mineral salts are necessary also to the nutrition of man and other animals; are they not part of his food?

This is a plausible argument, and the conclusion suggested is borne out by the facts so far presented. But there *are* two groups of substances involved in nutrition. A plant could not live only on the materials provided by the soil even if this were well fertilized and included all the essential elements; *photosynthesis also must occur.* The substances of which glucose is a sample are used in a unique way in both plants and animals, a way in which the salts of the earth cannot be used: they *supply the energy* which runs the machinery of life.

Think for a minute of an automobile with an empty fuel tank. All the necessary parts are there, perfectly arranged and coordinated; but nothing happens. The release of energy is needed to impel the pistons and turn the crankshaft, to animate the whole complex machine. Likewise a clock will not run if its spring is not wound, its weights not lifted, or electricity not supplied; some form of energy is needed, that provided by a coiled strip of steel, by gravity, or by an electrical current, depending upon the construction of the clock. And a cell, a minute and organized bit of protoplasm, is in the same plight. All its activity, its manufacture of auxin and enzymes and other things, its production of new protoplasm, its formation of walls, its division, its enlargement, the motion of its protoplasm—all these require energy. Magnesium, iron, all the necessary materials may be present; yet no chlorophyll will be formed without the application of energy. And the only source of energy for living cells is found in the substances we call foods. Not in calcium nitrate or in carbon dioxide or in magnesium sulphate; only in such things as sugar and starch, fat and protein. Electrical energy or heat cannot be substituted for foods, any more than we could cause an old-fashioned clock to run by sending an electric current through the weights.

How is energy obtained from sugar? We can burn it, and it will release energy in the form of heat; in the process it is changed to carbon dioxide and water. But obviously this cannot occur in living cells. In protoplasm a process occurs, at ordinary temperatures, which has some things in common with burning. In this process sugar breaks down into carbon dioxide and water, and energy is released. Indeed it is customary to refer to the process as "burning"; to speak of "burning up" foods in our bodies. Some of the energy is released as heat; but not all of it, even in a warm-blooded animal; and very little in plants. The rest of the energy that appears is "chemical energy," which is responsible for the chemical work done by the cell. Just as the energy released by exploding gasoline is responsible for the motion of the pistons in an engine, so the energy released by sugar as it is transformed into simpler substances is responsible for the combining of molecules in protoplasm, for the manufacture of new cellulose, for all the kinds of work mentioned above. The cell is a machine, and food the fuel which drives it. The process which releases the energy is called respiration.* It is brought about at ordinary temperatures in living cells by some of that class of indispensables, the enzymes.

In respiration glucose is changed into carbon dioxide and water: the very materials from which it was first formed in a leaf. An equation may be written for respiration which is exactly the reverse of that used on page 78 to symbolize photosynthesis: just point the arrow in the other direction. Free oxygen is used in the process, instead of being formed. It is not to be wondered at that this process is the opposite of photosynthesis also in its relation

---

* The term is unfortunate, for the physician uses it to refer to our breathing, to the activity of our lungs, to the passage of gases through certain internal spaces. In this sense plants do not respire; they do not breathe; indeed many animals (fish, for example) also do not breathe. But respiration in the biological sense refers to the chemical change of food which brings about the release of energy; it occurs in all cells; it is not the same as breathing, though with us it depends on breathing.

to energy: photosynthesis requires a supply of energy from the outside—the energy of light; respiration releases energy within the cell.

Respiration occurs *in all living cells all the time*; if it ceases, the machine stops working, the cell is dead. This being so, it must occur also in the very cells that carry on photosynthesis. One of these cells may be manufacturing glucose and oxygen from carbon dioxide and water and at the same time using oxygen in the breaking down of glucose into carbon dioxide and water. Obviously if both processes go on at the same rate, the glucose and oxygen made by photosynthesis will be used up in respiration; the carbon dioxide liberated in respiration will be used in photosynthesis; all within the one cell. There will be no net change in the contents of the cell: no glucose will be accumulated and no carbon dioxide, water, or oxygen will be exchanged with the outside world. But this, of course, does not happen; otherwise the only kind of living cell that could exist would be one which contained chlorophyll* —and even it would have to suspend operations for the night. Actually photosynthesis, in the bright hours of the growing season, goes on at a much greater rate than respiration; so that the latter is entirely masked in those cells which are busy making food.† A great excess of food is made over what the green cell uses; sufficient to supply that cell with energy during the night; sufficient for all the other cells of the plant to use and for some parts of the plant to accumulate in swollen tubers or in fruits or seeds; sufficient for the animal world as well.

Other foods may be used in respiration. If proteins or fats are used, the products formed will not be simply carbon dioxide and water. The nitrogen of the proteins will, of course, appear in the wastes which are formed, perhaps in ammonia; the sulphur perhaps in the ill-smelling gas hydrogen sulphide. Respiration has been simplified above by apparently limiting it to the break-down of

---

* Or some equivalent means of manufacturing food from the raw materials; a few kinds of bacteria, though they have no chlorophyll, make their food.

† The cell uses up all the carbon dioxide liberated in respiration and more besides which is taken from the outer world; and forms all the oxygen used in respiration and more besides which is given off into the outer world. Only a small part of the food which it makes is consumed in its own respiration.

glucose; in reality it is an extremely complex process and may occur in a variety of forms.

Some of the most interesting of these are called anaerobic.* It was remarked above that oxygen is used in the respiration of glucose; our own experience confirms this statement, at least for ourselves; and it is usually true also of plants. Cells, however, are often able to respire in the absence of free oxygen. The products will then be different, since the proportions of the various kinds of atoms that take part in the reaction are different. In the absence of free oxygen there will not be sufficient atoms of oxygen to allow all the carbon atoms to form carbon dioxide; instead some of the carbon with considerable hydrogen and a little oxygen may form such things as ethyl alcohol (C_2H_5OH). This is the basis for the importance of yeast. Yeast is a microscopic plant, and fermentation is the result of its respiration; it occurs beneath the surface of a liquid or a mixture of dough where free oxygen is scarce; it forms carbon dioxide (which raises the bread and makes the liquor bubble); and alcohol (which passes off from the bread in the baking, but forms a desired ingredient of the beverage). Other forms of fermentation are used in industry to produce various other substances. And such phenomena as the souring of milk or the production of vinegar are based on similar processes: on the respiration of minute organisms, which obtain in this way the energy which keeps them alive.

When scientists began to study foods, they found them only in living things, organisms (or in their corpses); they called them organic, supposing that they could only be made in living protoplasm through some sort of chemistry denied to the laboratory, peculiar to life, vitalistic. The barrier has long since been broken down. The chemist can make some sorts of foods in his flasks and test-tubes (it is expensive, and impractical for any purpose other than the pursuit of knowledge). But the name sticks. We still speak of organic compounds—foods and related substances—as distinct from the inorganic substances that form most of the

---

* *a-* or *an-* in Greek signifies "not" or "without"; the rest of the word is from the Greek for "air" and for "life" (*bi-* as in "biology"); "living without air."

earth's crust: water, the gases of the air, the metals, the rocks, and so on. We have books on and courses in organic chemistry and inorganic chemistry. The difference is not, however, very sharp. For the purposes of biology (though not always of chemistry), it is sufficient to say that organic substances have larger and more complex molecules which always contain carbon, that they will burn and yield energy, that many of them will yield energy also in living cells. Respiration is a breaking-down of organic substances into materials which are at least partly inorganic. Photosynthesis is a synthesis of an organic compound from inorganic materials. The cycles of the elements may be viewed as a constant passage from the inorganic to the organic form, and back again; with accompanying changes in energy content.

There, in short, is the secret of life: a continual flow of energy obtained from food. The principal use which plants and animals make of food is to *destroy* it—to change it into things which are not foods, wastes which cannot supply energy to protoplasm. Yet the supply of food is not thereby endangered; for the green plant undertakes the task of rebuilding food from the wastes—its own wastes and those of all other organisms besides. To do this requires energy from some source outside the cycle; and this comes from the sun. So in a sense the sun runs the whole scheme; it supplies the energy used in building food, and by virtue of this energy the food can itself deliver energy when it breaks down again. (So a pump supplies energy to water when it elevates it into a tank; and the water liberates energy again when it flows down again from the tank.) There is truth, then, in the figurative statement that we all live on "bottled sunlight." Our fields and pastures and orchards, our vegetable gardens are devices for trapping sunlight, most of it ultimately to be converted into the energy by which we live.

THE KINDS OF FOOD

It is commonly asserted that only green cells can make food; only cells which contain chlorophyll. This is one of those half-truths, those over-simplified statements that conceal what really happens. The fact is that *all living cells* can and do manu-facture food. This truth, apparently so contrary to what is taught in the schools, merits some discussion.

Foods are of a pleasing variety; we do not (and indeed could not) live on glucose alone. Glucose is one of a large group of substances called sugars (our table sugar is sucrose). The sugars have numerous relatives, all, like themselves, built upon atoms of carbon, all containing hydrogen and oxygen (mostly in the proportions of 2 to 1, as in water). The most familiar of these are the starches and the celluloses. Together this entire group of substances is called the carbohydrates.*

But is cellulose a food? Tom Sawyer and Huck Finn did manage to swallow the sawdust—but it did not contribute to their well-being. We are unable to digest cellulose, and therefore it is un-available as a source of energy to our cells. But certain bacteria and fungi—the so-called "lower plants"—can do what we cannot. This is obvious when we see the "brackets" of fungi projecting from a tree-trunk; these are the reproductive parts of a fungus whose body of delicate threads is within the trunk and ultimately causes its downfall; these branching threads penetrate the wood everywhere, digesting it and absorbing the products. They form enzymes which we do not. The same is true of the bacteria which bring about the decay of fallen timber or of dead leaves. If such enzymes did not occur, all the trees that have ever grown, all the leaves that have ever fallen would still litter the earth, except as they had been removed by fire. Cellulose, even cellulose impregnated with lignin, is therefore a food, at least for some organisms.

Another class of foods formed of the same three elements is the fats. This term includes the oils, which are simply more liquid fats; but not the so-called "essential oils," such as oil of peppermint, of lavender, of camphor, which belong to quite a different chemical group; they flavor our food but are not themselves used as food.

---

* Hydrated carbon, *i.e.* carbon joined with water; a somewhat fanciful name, which calls attention to the proportions of hydrogen and oxygen in most of them.

Fats differ from carbohydrates in having much less oxygen in proportion to their carbon. They are found in every living cell.

A third large class of foods, like the preceding groups universally present, is the proteins. These contain nitrogen besides carbon, hydrogen, and oxygen; and those of plants contain sulphur. The nuclear proteins contain also phosphorus. The molecules of proteins are the largest known, enormous and complex things consisting of long strings of atoms from which dangle "side-chains" of yet more atoms.

Almost all these foods are insoluble in water. Of the carbohydrates the starches and celluloses will not dissolve in water. The inability of fats to mix with water is proverbial; one can form an emulsion by shaking them up together, but not a true solution. The proteins are almost all colloidal in structure and do not form true solutions. The importance of digestion is again emphasized by these facts. *None of these insoluble foods can enter or leave a living cell.* They are all made in the cells in which they are found. Only the products of digestion can move from cell to cell. Carbohydrates are changed by digestion into sugars; fats into fatty acids and glycerol; proteins into amino acids; all these things can dissolve in water and move through the protoplasm and its bounding membranes. All these changes are brought about by particular enzymes, each of which seems to have been created for a particular transformation.

From what do the living cells of plants make foods? One of the requisite building-blocks is some sort of carbohydrate made in the leaves and distributed to the other parts through the phloem. This organic material is combined, in every living cell of a green plant, with materials obtained from the soil, the inorganic nutrients that rise in the stream of sap, salts of nitrogen, of sulphur, of phosphorus, and the rest. Thus the cells make their foods, their reserves, their building material, each within itself; forming also new cell walls, new protoplasm, and perhaps other new parts.

This manufacture of food that occurs in all living plant cells differs in one respect—one all-important respect—from that which occurs under the auspices of chlorophyll and light in the leaves: cells that lack chlorophyll must be supplied with *at least one* *organic substance.* In photosynthesis *all the raw materials are inorganic.* This is the true and accurate version of the misstatement quoted above: only in cells containing chlorophyll can food be made from nothing but inorganic ingredients. But *all* living cells make food, providing they have at least some organic substance to start with. This is true of animal as well as of plant cells: the manufacture of fat from other organic substances, such as sugar, is only too familiar in our own bodies. Animal cells are less versatile than plant cells in the use of inorganic materials; they must have their nitrogen also supplied in an organic compound.* But *all* cells, plant and animal, are indebted to photosynthesis for the necessary organic ingredient in their syntheses. In this sense it is true that all the food of the world is traceable to the mesophyll of green leaves or to other cells which have chlorophyll and are exposed to light.

Besides the foods proper, living bodies must have those substances sometimes called the accessory foods: the vitamins. They are necessary in very small amounts, but without them life cannot continue. That animals must have vitamins has been known for some time. Captain Cook demonstrated that lemons contain something which will prevent scurvy; early in the twentieth century this something was isolated and named vitamin C or ascorbic acid. Now everyone knows that we are dependent upon plants for most of our vitamins. It is not so generally understood that plants themselves need them: a fact more recently demonstrated. This discovery resulted partly from the culture of fungi in purified nutrient solutions; partly from the attempt to grow roots in such solutions without the green tops to which they are normally attached. The latter feat was not achieved (the roots would not grow indefinitely) until thiamine—vitamin B_1—was added to the solution. Normally this is supplied by the green parts of the plant and transmitted to other parts. When this was realized, and when the necessary techniques were perfected, it was shown that other vitamins also are necessary to plant life. All living things need vitamins; apparently they all use them in much the same ways. They are essential to the use of food, to normal growth, and to other functions. Some

---

* This is true also of some fungi.

fungi, like animals, are unable to make all their own vitamins, and must have an external source. Green plants apparently make their own—and ours.

FOOD COMES IN PACKAGES

One of the more engaging habits of plants is their way of accumulating food in particular parts of their bodies.* We find food concentrated in fruits and seeds, in tubers and bulbs; and we make use of these richly furnished parts to our own advantage. Were it not for these packages of food we should have to subsist mainly on the flesh of cows or other animals which can pass through their capacious stomachs the immense quantities of ordinary leaves and stems necessary to furnish a sufficiency of food.

Civilization, indeed, probably had its origin when man, besides hunting and pasturing his food, learned to cultivate it. Wheat and the other cereals (rice, oats, barley, maize, etc.) are among the oldest of our crops; their domestication preceded the beginning of history and we are not even sure where they originated nor from what wild ancestors. Their usefulness depends on their grains, which are packed with carbohydrates and contain fats and proteins also. Other seeds are rich in fat or oil, as those of flax, of cotton, of peanuts, of castor-bean, of coconut, of walnut and pecan, of almonds.† The seeds of flowering plants are generally contained in some sort of fruit, by which the botanist understands not only the edible fruits which we all know but also various hard and inedible

* This is generally spoken of as the "storage" of food; and so, indeed, it is. But when we credit a plant with "storing" food, perhaps for the use of the next generation, we again fall into the error, already mentioned several times in this book, of speaking of plants as if they could foresee the future and could act accordingly. Perhaps they do; but such aspects of life are as yet intractable to scientific analysis and should not be tolerated in scientific description.

† The grain of the grasses is a seed surrounded by a layer known as the pericarp which is fused to the outer surface of the seed coat. The shell of a coconut is the inner part of the fruit; the seed coat is the hard brown skin on the surface of the meat, the endosperm. Much the same is true of almonds and walnuts and pecans, except that there is no endosperm and the seed coat is appressed to the surface of the cotyledons.

Fruits are described and illustrated on pp. 180-188.

pods, capsules, nuts, and so forth. Apples and pears, cherries and plums and peaches, grapes, bananas, berries of all kinds, dates, figs, mangoes at once come to mind as fruits which contain quantities of food. Melons and squashes and pumpkins and cucumber and tomatoes and egg-plant and string-beans which we may think of as "vegetables," are also fruits. The food in these useful objects is most often sugar. Bananas are rich in starch. Olives and avocados contain oil.

Primitive man doubtless scrabbled in the earth for edible parts of plants; we grow varieties selected through years of breeding to produce larger and more palatable roots and tubers. Carrots and turnips and parsnips and beets are main roots, tap roots, principally composed of parenchyma in which more or less food may be present. Sweet potatoes are lateral or branch roots transformed into tubers and literally packed with food; the vascular tissue follows an irregular course through the nutritious mass. Dahlia tubers are similar. The prize among edible roots is doubtless the man-of-the-earth, the root of a relative of the sweet potato and morning-glory, which may reach several feet in length and weigh 15 pounds; it has been used as food by Indians—and by hogs. Many roots are of enormous importance to man. Cassava, the tuberous root of a plant called manihot, is the staple diet of the natives of South America; it is prepared in various ways and eaten several times a day. Taro, the root of a plant in the same family as calla lily and skunk cabbage, is said to be "practically indispensable to tropical natives."

Stems also are important. White ("Irish") potatoes are branches of the stem, for all that they grow horizontally and underground. A potato cut across reveals a ring of vascular bundles (seen as small dots) not far from the outer surface; an immense pith occupies most of the tuber. This is the arrangement found in stems, not in roots (p. 63). At and near the end farthest from the main stem there are buds—the "eyes" from which new branches may sprout. Each bud is in the axil of a leaf, as usual; a leaf reduced to a mere ridge, the eyebrow for the eye.

In some kinds of plants the main stem is tuberous instead of a branch; it is then usually known as a corm. Examples are gladiolus,

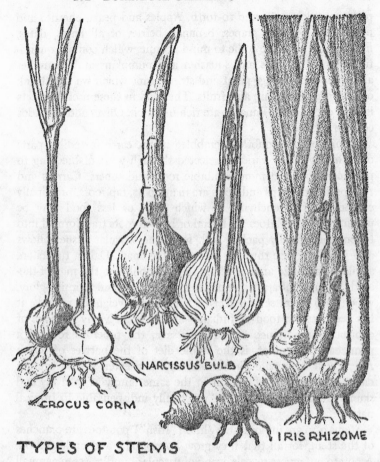

NARCISSUS BULB

CROCUS CORM

IRIS RHIZOME

TYPES OF STEMS

crocus, cyclamen. In others the main stem grows horizontally and underground (or at the surface). This sort of stem, called a rhizome, is characteristic of most blue violets, of iris, of bloodroot and Solomon's seal, and of many other plants. Such stems contain an abundance of food, though they do not usually appear on our tables.

Some of these tubers (which may be roots or stems) and rhizomes (which are stems) are known as bulbs. Botanists, however, reserve this word for the beautiful structure exemplified by the common onion, and found also in daffodils, tulips, hyacinths, and many lilies. It is really a sort of compressed and enlarged bud; the stem forms a disc at the base and the thickened overlapping leaves and leaf-bases stand on the upper side of the disc. Because the stem does not elongate, the leaves remain closely imbricated. In the center, where the growing tip of the stem would be looked for, the apical meristem, we usually find a flowering stalk, which bears leaves of a different type, or perhaps no leaves at all.

So we find that almost all kinds of plants have developed some sort of specially constructed, enlarged part in which food accumulates; food which in nature helps to start the new season's growth, or the next generation. Man has appropriated to his own uses the plants with the largest and most palatable food-storing parts, whether they are seeds, fruits, roots, stems, or leaves; has domesticated them and improved them almost beyond recognition; has transformed the face of nature by substituting neat rows of these plants for the random wilderness; and turns them to many delicious uses in his ingenious cookery.

5

⋘⋘⋘

The Trunk of a
Tree

THE BARK IS ALIVE

In the preceding pages a story has been told, a picture
has been painted. A plant has emerged from a seed, enlarged to
many hundred times its original size; thrust down and formed a
root system which ramifies through the earth and taps its wealth;
carried its shoot into the air, producing leaves which make food—
food which is carried to all other parts, which forms the new substance of the plant and which supplies the energy which runs the
whole organism. The plant thus depicted is largely water. Its parts
contain masses of watery parenchyma cells, among which run the
tougher strings of the vascular elements. Wax on the outer skin,
and automatically regulated openings in the leaves help to conserve
the water which the roots acquire in their questing. But, in spite
of these structures, a stream of water moves through the plant most
of the time—a stream enclosed by cells which are themselves mostly
water.

Many plants die after a brief season of growth; the result of all
the complicated activity heretofore described is, finally, a number
of seeds from which will emerge new plants, to repeat the cycle.
The production of flowers and fruit (to be described later, pages
137-141) may exhaust the life of such a plant; or the onset of frost
may kill it. But many other plants survive such events and live

from year to year. Some form rhizomes, bulbs, tubers, and the like which remain alive after the leaves and flowering stems have disappeared, forming new aerial parts with the return of the growing season. Some merely shed their leaves; their stiff woody stems, their sealed buds withstand the rigors of winter or of a dry season and burst into new growth when temperatures rise or when water is again plentiful. Some retain their leaves, even in severe climates, from year to year; they are usually leaves of a very special structure. These perennial plants add to their bodies every season. Many of them not only add new lengths of stem and new branches, new lengths of roots and new roots, but they also increase in girth. Their stems and roots become thicker. A forest tree, as everyone knows, is mostly wood; not merely a cylinder of woody strings embedded in soft parenchyma, but a mass of hundreds of cubic feet of solid wood. Where does all this come from? How was it formed? What is the origin of the rough, scaly or plated or furrowed bark that covers the wood? Are all these parts alive? And where do the water and the food flow?

To answer such questions is difficult. It necessitates some further delving into plant anatomy, a technical and highly specialized branch of botany. A complete exposition of what is known as secondary growth in a stem or root (it is very rare in leaves, which are mostly short-lived) is impossible in an elementary treatment; but the main outlines of the process can be suggested, and thus a more rounded picture of the whole business of plant growth may be obtained.*

The key to all the changes embraced in secondary growth is the remarkable ability of plant cells to resume multiplication and growth, even after they have apparently ceased from such activities. This is particularly true of parenchyma cells, those thin-walled watery cells so abundant in all parts of a plant; but epidermal cells also will sometimes behave in the same way, and other kinds of cells also.

This happens, for example, in the epidermis of a young apple twig, and in that of roses, willows, oleander. Long after this outer

---

* But you may omit this part if you wish, without endangering your understanding of what follows.

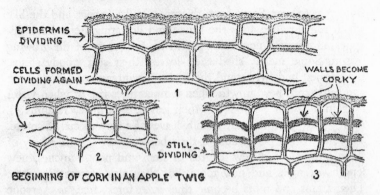

EPIDERMIS DIVIDING →

CELLS FORMED DIVIDING AGAIN

WALLS BECOME CORKY

1

2

STILL DIVIDING →

3

BEGINNING OF CORK IN AN APPLE TWIG

layer has taken shape, late in the growing season and after growth has apparently ceased in it and in neighboring layers, its cells begin to divide again. The new cell walls are parallel to the surface of the twig. The result is that the epidermis comes to consist of two layers of cells instead of one, then of three or four layers, finally of many layers; a many-tiered sheath or covering is built up around the stem, outside the cortex. Just as transverse divisions in the tip of the stem form long files of cells, so these parallel divisions in the bark form blocks of cells side by side, very evident in microscopic view.

As this happens, the appearance of the surface of the twig changes; it becomes brown and hard. This change corresponds to a transformation of the cells at and near the surface; their walls become impregnated with a fatty material (like cutin) called suberin. Then these cells die; for suberin makes the walls impervious to water, and the protoplasm which has encased itself in a waterproof sheath can no longer be nourished by adjacent cells. This dead brown mass through which water will not easily pass is what we know as cork.

These layers of new cells do not always have their origin in the epidermis. In oaks, elms, maples, the first divisions may occur in the cells just beneath the epidermis; in rhododendron, in cells deeper within the cortex. The result is the same. As the layer of cork develops, any cells exterior to it will be split, starved, desiccated; the cork will take their place as the outer layer of the stem.

New cork cells are continually added, from the *inside*, by the division of the inner cells, which do not become suberized.* Other, similar layers of dividing cells also appear, within the first, in the cortex. They add new layers of cork, which as they thicken push the older ones further out and split them asunder. As the cork becomes older it is thus cleft into ridges or scales or blocks in a pattern characteristic of the kind of plant. The bark of flowering dogwood forms small squarish segments, while that of an ash appears in a network of long ridges; the outer layers of ponderosa pine and of sycamore separate into scales of various shapes and colors. Cork is of various textures; that of a species of oak native to the Mediterranean lands is what we fashion into stoppers and flooring and insulation. This is the material in which Robert Hooke saw cells and gave them a name. They were only the cavities where living cells had once been; but this layer of suberized cell walls is a far more efficient covering for the stem than the epidermis with its microscopic layer of wax. Not only does it prevent undue loss of water, it is a shield against the invasion of parasites. And it can grow with the growth of the wood within.

Further consideration of the behavior of bark, that apparently hard, inert covering of a trunk or branch, shows that it really contains living cells. If a wire is fastened around a growing woody stem—a guy wire to a telephone pole, or a strand of a fence—one will usually see, after a year or two, a bulge above the wire. The constriction limits the development of the stem and prevents additions to the bark at that level. Food coming down from the leaves collects above the wire and stimulates those parts to overgrowth; for the phloem, which carries the food, is in the bark. If the stem is girdled—that is, if a ring of bark is entirely removed, all around the trunk and down to the wood—the plant will ultimately die. No food from the leaves can pass the gap and reach the roots, and these will gradually starve; they have inorganic materials from the soil but no organic substance from the green parts. When the

---

* The dividing cells form what is known technically as the phellogen, from Greek words meaning "cork" and "generate." The cork layer itself is also known as the phelloderm, the "cork skin." All this apparatus, phellogen, phelloderm, and other cells which may be formed, constitute the periderm, the "skin around."

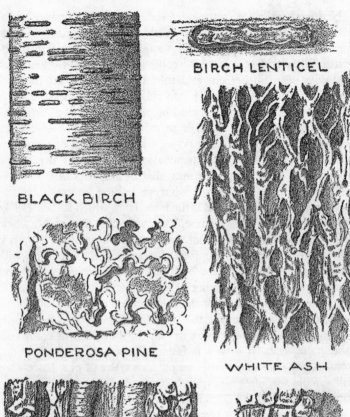

BIRCH LENTICEL

BLACK BIRCH

PONDEROSA PINE

WHITE ASH

CORK CALLUS WOOD CALLUS CORK

WOUND HEALING IN RED OAK

FLOWERING
DOGWOOD

BARK

roots die they cease to take in water and no longer send it up the stem; and the whole plant shortly dies for lack of water. This is the lazy man's way of removing trees; all he needs to do is to girdle the stems—and wait. After a few years he will have only the dead stumps to deal with. Goats that are allowed to run loose in a grove of trees often have the same effect; and rabbits are the bane of many a young sapling. It is inadvisable for the same reason even to leave on your nursery stock the wire which fastens the label to one of the branches.

Here and there on the smooth bark of young branches you will see small dots or transverse streaks, slightly elevated above the surface. These are caused by masses of parenchyma cells formed within the bark which break through to the outside. They are called lenticels. Their size, shape, and distribution are characteristic of the kind of plant; the narrow transverse lenticels of wild cherry and of black birch are familiar means of identification of those trees. In most kinds of trees, however, the roughness of the bark soon obscures the lenticels. The existence of these patches of living cells in contact with air probably makes it easier for the living cells of the inner layers of the bark to obtain oxygen and so to respire. Another activity of the living parts of the bark, intermittent but none the less important, is the healing of wounds. Almost every gardener, certainly every one who walks much in the woods, has seen the scar left in a tree-trunk by lightning: a rent in the bark from top to bottom, often spiraling around the trunk. The living cells within the bark which are exposed at the edges of the scar begin to divide, forming an irregular mass of cells called callus which gradually projects over the naked wood. Little by little it invades the exposed surface, like a wave spreading over a dry beach; cells busily dividing within; the outer cells becoming suberized, forming a more or less waterproof protecting layer. If all goes well, if no invading fungi cause a rot in the wood beneath, if no birds or insects seize the opportunity to excavate dwellings for themselves, in a year or two the two edges of the callus will meet, and nothing will remain of the injury but a long narrow scar in the bark.

THE WOOD GROWS

Within this surprisingly complicated and essential bark is the wood; all the rest of a tree-trunk is wood.* Here is the source of our lumber, the material from which we build our houses, construct our furniture, make handles for tools, boxes to hold goods, frames for pictures—thousands of familiar things. Its characteristics are known to all. It will split more or less easily in one direction, but not at right angles to this, for it is made of long fibers lying side by side. It has various lines and bands and flecks and curls referred to as grain, often forming a pleasing pattern. It is of various colors and degrees of hardness or porousness, and can be variously sawed, stained, oiled, waxed, polished, painted. Botanically it is all xylem. Xylem varies greatly in different kinds of trees; but it conforms to the general description set forth on pages 61, 62.

We perhaps think of wood most readily in terms of flat planks or boards of various widths and thicknesses and lengths. But in nature it forms a cylinder. If we cut across this cylinder we see that it is actually many cylinders, one within the other, all, of course, so tightly fitted as to form one solid block; for the cross section is marked by concentric rings. Intersecting the rings and radiating from the center are straight lines referred to as rays.† Some of these run from the center to the bark, diverging as they go; others begin farther out, in the spaces left by the divergence of the longer ones.

If the wood is split through its middle, the concentric cylinders which form the rings in the cross section give us long straight parallel lines running lengthwise in the cut surface. The rays are now parallel to the cut surface; they may appear as shining areas or flecks here and there. If a slab of wood is sawed off from the outside the rays will be intersected more or less at right angles and will be seen as short vertical lines (each ray being of a limited depth); while the rings now lie in the plane of the cut and give a

---

* The microscopic pith which is present in the young stem from which the trunk develops becomes hard and woodlike, as it is impregnated with various wastes.

† The picture here presented is good for most kinds of wood; but there are kinds in which these figures cannot be seen.

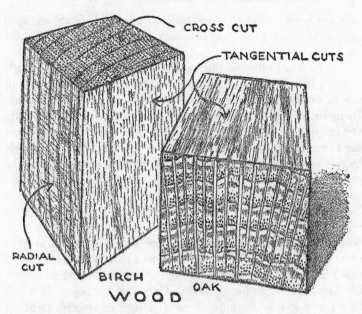

CROSS CUT

TANGENTIAL CUTS

RADIAL CUT

BIRCH
WOOD
OAK

more indefinite figure. Of course many intermediate cuts are possible, each giving a new view of the intersected rays and rings and forming the many patterns of grain that give wood its charm. Since the tree is not a perfect cylinder, various irregularities, particularly in the rings, cause attractive swirls and curves in the grain.

But an excursion into the technology of wood will not answer the question: where does it all come from? How is it formed? Certainly it differs greatly in form as it does in size from the first xylem formed in the stem, the primary xylem just below the region of elongation, that cylinder of separate small strings of lignified tubes and fibers.

Again the key to the problem is the ability of cells to resume division. In this case the cells are small parenchyma cells; they lie just outside the xylem in the young stem—on the side towards the epidermis, between the xylem and phloem. As they divide, the new walls (like those in the cork-forming layers of the bark) are parallel to the surface of the stem. This division occurs not only in cells of the vascular bundles but in the parenchyma cells between adjacent bundles; so that *a complete cylinder of dividing cells* soon extends all around the stem and encloses the xylem (and the pith also).

The further history of this layer is much like that of the cork-forming layers described above; but the layer forms its new cells mostly *towards the center of the stem*, not towards the epidermis. By division the single layer of cells becomes a layer of many cells, one cell outside another: a cylindrical sheath of cells which encloses the xylem and pith. As in the bark, the cells thus formed are side by side in blocks which radiate from the center of the stem. (The new cells of the wood are consequently arranged in the same way: in lines which radiate from the center.) As this sheath becomes thicker, as more cells are added to it by division, the *inner* cells cease dividing, and enlarge instead, developing thick walls with peculiar markings; in short, they become vessels and fibers and the other elements of the xylem. In this way a new layer, a cylinder of wood is formed, just *outside* the old xylem strips, just *inside* the dividing layer which has formed it. Once this has begun, it is easy to see how it will continue: layer after layer of wood is built up, the youngest always on the outside; but the dividing layer still surrounds *all* the wood. This is the origin of the massive trunk of a tree, of its complex column of wood.

So in a growing stem we find dividing cells (or cells capable of

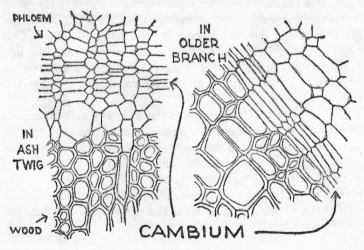

PHLOEM

IN OLDER BRANCH

IN ASH TWIG

WOOD

CAMBIUM

continued division) not only at the apex and in the axils of the leaves but in two (or more) concentric cylinders within: one (or more) near the outside, in the bark, busy forming the hard outer covering, the cork of the bark; the other just under the bark, at the surface of the wood, busy adding to the wood. Similar layers are formed in roots. Each of these layers of dividing cells is called a cambium. All the cambiums (and any other similar layers in the plan) are called secondary meristems; to distinguish them from the meristems at the apices of stems and roots and in the axils of leaves, which are called the primary meristems. The first structure of a stem or root and all the leaves, as we have seen, is made of cells which were formed by division at the apex, in the primary meristem. The parts which make up this first structure are called the primary tissues. Now we have seen the addition of new layers, formed by the secondary meristems, the cambiums. These parts are, naturally, called secondary tissues. The cork of the bark is secondary; so is most of the wood of a stem—all except those original thin strips in the vascular bundles. In general the primary tissues add to the length of stems and roots, while the secondary tissues add to their thickness.

Secondary thickening occurs to some extent in many herbaceous stems—even in annual stems which will not continue to add new layers year after year. In a cross section of a sunflower stem, for instance, you will see a ring of dividing cells, a cambium, extending all around the stem, passing through all the vascular bundles, lying outside the xylem. Just inside this ring you will see a layer of wood. Not very much wood, to be sure; nothing of interest to a lumberman; but wood nevertheless, and able to fulfill the functions of wood in a plant. It adds new strengthening material where it is most needed, and provides additional ducts through which water can reach the expanding canopy of leaves above.

THE WOOD WRITES ITS HISTORY

The results of the activity of the cambiums are, of course, best seen in the great trees of our forests, which may add new wood for hundreds—even thousands—of years. The beginning of a year's growth, the first wood laid down in the spring, is usually

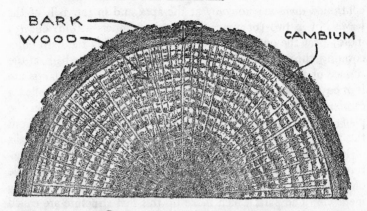

BARK
WOOD
CAMBIUM

OAK TRUNK

of a different character from that formed during the summer. The spring wood of the oaks, of elm and ash, for instance, contains most of the large vessels which are visible to the unaided eye, and which the forester and the lumberman often refer to as "pores." Since a complete new layer of wood, an entire cylinder, is formed in the spring, there may be a complete ring of these large pores in the cross section. This makes a visible band, a ring, in the wood—the annual ring which contributes so much to the grain of the wood. Such woods are called "ring-porous." Maple, poplar, beech, sycamore, magnolia, and other woods have their large pores scattered through the season's wood—they are "diffuse-porous." The woods of coniferous trees—pine, spruce, cedar, and the rest—have no vessels, and are sometimes called "non-porous."* Even diffuse-porous and non-porous woods, however, usually form cells of a different type in spring, as compared with those formed the preceding summer, so that "annual rings" are visible even without a ring of large pores.

As the wood gets thicker and thicker, the central parts, the older parts, usually become clogged with wastes and the water-ducts become stopped up. This wood, which often changes color and becomes very hard, is the "heartwood" so prized for fine furniture.

---

* These terms are unfortunate; for all wood is really porous. Most of the "pores"—i.e. the ducts in the wood—are visible only when magnified.

The outer, younger layers of wood, through which the transpiration stream continually rises to the leaves above, compose the "sapwood." It is common knowledge that a tree may continue to flourish and grow even when most of its trunk is hollow. The sapwood around the hollow is sufficient for the needs of the top, and so long as parasitic fungi do not invade it from the inside, so long as winds are not too severe, this shell may continue to act as efficiently as a solid trunk.

The thickness of the annual bands of wood varies with their position in the tree and with changes in their environment year by year. A drought will leave its mark on all the trees in the affected region, in the form of a narrow band. Forest fires may consume parts of a tree, which may survive and close the wound but still carries the scar within. So we may read on the cut surface of a stump or felled log some of the history of that part of the world, sometimes for hundreds of years. If we know when the tree was felled, and therefore when the outermost band of wood was formed, we can date all the rings by counting back from the outside.* The character of particular rings, thus dated, may often be correlated with old records of rainfall and other events, and with the recollections of old settlers—each confirming the other. Sometimes we find a band which is easy to identify, perhaps a wide ring between very narrow ones; having dated this and verified the fact that that was a year of abundant rainfall preceded and followed by unusually dry years, we can identify the same ring in other pieces of wood of unknown origin, and thus *determine the year in which they were cut*. Or, if we find the dated ring in a beam in an old building, we can determine within a few years when the building was erected; so botany has come to the aid of archaeology. From beams which we have thus dated we may assign dates to still older layers of wood in other beams and other buildings, and so work our way back to a remoter past. Andrew Ellicott Douglass used this method first in his study of climate and then in the archaeology of Indian ruins. He has assigned the date A.D. 700 to

---

* Except in certain places, as in the southwestern United States, where two periods of growth, corresponding to two distinct rainy seasons, may occur in one year.

some of these; and if his records and conclusions are correct, a civilization flourished in southwestern North America at the time Norman William was invading England. But the method is full of pitfalls and the results must not be blindly accepted. The factors concerned in the growth of wood are complex; there may have been more than one ring in a year; and the methods used in correlating the widths of rings from tree to tree are susceptible of possible error.

What of the phloem during all these changes in the wood? Does it remain unchanged while its sister-tissue, the xylem, undergoes such a tremendous growth? It must be recalled that the phloem, the all-important tissue through which the food moves, is *in the bark*. It is outside the wood; it forms part of the inner living layers of the bark. It also increases through the years. Secondary phloem is added by the cambium. The cambium which is just *outside* the wood is just *inside* the phloem. New layers of phloem are added *within* the older ones, pushing these farther out. But the older layers often get squashed in the process; and some of them are constantly becoming changed into part of the cork-forming apparatus, as already mentioned. So, all in all, the phloem does not become much thicker through the years. It remains a thin living layer which lines the rough outer cork of the bark; that delicate, often slimy layer to be seen when a willow twig is peeled in the spring. Thin as it is, it is vitally important in the life of the plant; if it is removed—the tree will die.

The preceding simplified account, though inadequate to give a complete and detailed picture of what goes on in the trunk of a tree—or a branch—will yet, perhaps, serve to convey some general impression of the complexity of a living being. To the operator of a bulldozer engaged in "improving" a piece of land, a tree is merely something to be pushed over with the demoniac power at his command; perhaps the woodsman, the pioneer, who had only an axe to clear his few acres in the wilderness had more respect for what he destroyed. Within that rough, inert shell of cork what activity there is! What innumerable divisions of minute protoplasmic units, slowly adding new layers in what seems to be a preordained pattern; what streaming of food through long narrow living tubes, what upward-flowing of sap through yet other tubes. Millions of millions of cells are there, all organized, all performing certain kinds of work—even dying to serve the general needs of the plant. We might perhaps compare the living trunk of a tree to a republic of cells; except that the cells do their work so much more harmoniously than the units of a man-constituted republic.

6

Propagating Plants

PLANTS ARE EASY TO PROPAGATE

When you want a new coleus plant from your old one, you need not plant seeds. Indeed it is usually hard to find seeds; and one cannot always predict just what will grow from them— the variety you have and want to multiply, or something else.

The usual method of propagation is simplicity itself. You cut off a length of stem just below a pair of leaves or a node where leaves once grew; from here up everything may be intact, if you wish: the whole upper part of the plant. You place this cut-off piece, or cutting, with the cut end in wet sand or moss or even in water; use a little of one of the "plant hormones"* if you like, to make results more sure. Shade the cutting and keep the air moist, so as to reduce loss of water to a minimum. After a week, if you take up the cutting carefully, you will find a cluster of roots projecting from the lower end, at and near the cut surface. The new plant may now be planted in ordinary soil, and, with reasonable care, it will continue to grow, forming new roots, stem, and leaves in the usual way.

The cutting, once merely a severed part of a plant, is now itself a complete plant, self-supporting, with all the parts its parent had, and is remarkably like that parent in the color and size of its leaves. In short, reproduction has resulted from your intervention in natural processes. A new living being has been created.

How is this possible? Very certainly the reproduction of animals

---

* They are sold by various proprietary names. See p. 23.

cannot be brought about in this way; that is, of the warm-blooded animals with which we are ordinarily familiar. You cannot cut off a portion of your pet—his tail, say—and induce it to become a complete new individual. Yet you can do just this sort of thing with a great variety of plants. The reason lies in two facts in the structure of plants which have already been noticed: (1) the existence of meristems at the tips of stems and roots, in the axils of leaves, and elsewhere, which can continue almost indefinitely to add to the stature of the plant; (2) the presence of large numbers of relatively unspecialized cells, particularly the parenchyma. The parts of the new coleus plant—leaves, stem, roots—are formed in two ways: (1) by the continued activity of meristems of the parent plant, which are now meristems of the cutting; (2) by the return of certain mature cells (usually parenchyma) to a meristematic condition. Neither of these thing happens to any extent in the animals we usually encounter (including man). Groups of cells which correspond to the meristems of plants are confined, in animals, to certain parts of their bodies and produce only certain special kinds of cells; red blood cells, for instance. And the animal body, which grows to a limited size and a limited number of parts, does not contain unspecialized cells corresponding to parenchyma in any abundance.

When you make a stem cutting in the way described above, a cutting of coleus or geranium or rose or willow or philodendron or chrysanthemum or sunflower or dogwood or lilac or one of several hundred other well-known plants, the apical meristem, which is part of the terminal bud, is scarcely affected by the operation (provided the supply of water is not seriously impeded). It continues to add new cells to the stem, and to form new leaves, in the way previously described (p. 38). Even if you have cut off the top of the stem (and this cut is generally made just *above* a pair of leaves), growth will continue, new stems and leaves will appear from the buds in the axils of the upper leaves; there will probably be—in coleus—two branches growing on the cutting instead of one. These meristems that continue their activities no matter what happens to the part of the plant which bears them— or are stimulated into renewed activity by the operation—these may be called "persistent" meristems; they endure, they persist in their usual behavior.

The roots, on the other hand, grow where roots do not normally grow; they are "adventitious." When the piece of stem is cut off from its base, some chemical and physical changes, the nature of which is as yet unknown, stimulate certain parenchyma cells within the stem to start dividing. Such cells are mature cells, differentiated (they are different from cells of xylem, phloem, and the rest); but not very highly differentiated (they do not have exaggerated length nor peculiarly thickened or perforated walls or any such extreme characteristics). Nevertheless they *are* differentiated as compared with meristematic cells; and their return to the meristematic condition which they had seemingly abandoned, a change spoken of as dedifferentiation, is sufficiently surprising.*

This happens also to the cells at the cut surface (except those that are injured or destroyed by the propagator's knife); they also begin to divide, forming a mass of cells which covers the cut end and whose outer walls frequently become more or less suberized. This layer which closes the wound is called the callus.† The new roots come from dividing cells which organize themselves into definite apical meristems—the tips of roots. This may happen in the callus itself; more frequently it happens in the parenchyma within the stem, near the vascular bundles. Moreover, certain *other* cells divide, change their shape and the nature of their walls, and become vascular ducts which connect those of the new roots with the old vascular system of the stem.

In an ordinary stem cutting both the phenomena are illustrated which make propagation easy for plants: persistence of meristems and dedifferentiation. The apical meristems and axillary meristems persist and form new stem and leaves; the roots come from dedifferentiated cells of the stem. But some species will form new plants from nothing more than detached leaves, or even parts of leaves; and various combinations of meristematic activity and dedifferen-

---

* This change has already been noticed in these pages, in the formation of cambium; see pp. 106, 111.

† This term has already been used for the mass of cells which closes a wound in the bark of a tree; see p. 109.

tiation may occur. Since most mature leaves have no meristems (all their dividing cells having finally ceased division and matured; most leaves do not increase indefinitely in size), we should expect to find that some of them produce the new individuals entirely by dedifferentiation of some of their mature cells; and this is true.

That favorite house-plant, the African violet, is a good example of reproduction by leaves. It is well known that if a detached leaf is placed with its stalk in water or wet sand or moss, roots and (later) a bud will appear, and a new plant may be obtained. Microscopic study has revealed that the roots arise from parenchyma cells much as in the stem of coleus; in particular from the parenchyma cells (either in the stalk or in the blade of the leaf) which lie near the vascular cells of the veins. The buds, however, come from cells of the epidermis; more highly differentiated cells but still, evidently, capable of dedifferentiation. Leaves of the Rex begonia will form new plants in just the same way. They may be obtained even from portions of the blade of these species, simply by putting such a piece of the leaf in a covered dish on some moist paper. A certain crassula has even more striking powers of dedifferentiation; it forms all the new parts, leaves and stem as well as roots, from the epidermis of a detached leaf.

But not all leaves which reproduce do it in this way. At the other extreme are some of the species of bryophyllum. One kind commonly grown in greenhouses (it is tropical in origin) has a crenate leaf, i.e. a leaf regularly notched all around the margin, the parts between the notches being rounded. Break a leaf off and keep it in moist air (in a covered dish, for instance, lying on some wet filter-paper), and a new plantlet, complete with two leaves, a stem, and two roots will shortly appear in each notch. Sometimes, indeed, they become visible even while the leaf is still attached to the plant, and another species regularly bears an array of such young plants around each of its leaves, high in the air and with no immediate prospect of reaching the ground. Research into these leaves has disclosed the surprising fact that the little plants are there—in the notches—from the beginning, whether or not they enlarge sufficiently to be seen. They can be traced back to a time when the entire leaf was a meristematic structure composed of

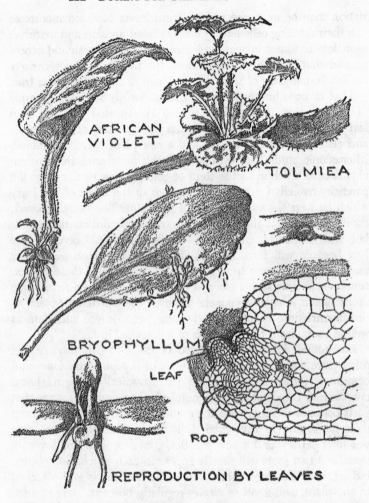

AFRICAN VIOLET

TOLMIEA

BRYOPHYLLUM

LEAF

ROOT

REPRODUCTION BY LEAVES

rapidly dividing cells. As all the other cells of the leaf—the vast majority—matured, differentiated, became epidermis, palisade, spongy tissue, veins, these small lumps of cells in the notches did not mature. They remained young, i.e. meristematic, organizing themselves into an apical meristem with two rudimentary leaves—the beginnings of a bud—and two root-tips. Under suitable magnification the tiny bud can be discovered in each notch, replacing epidermis at that point; the root-tips are buried within the tissues of the leaf. In this condition the entire little plant usually becomes dormant. It has been called, appropriately, a "foliar embryo."

The young plants of bryophyllum, therefore, are entirely the result of a persistent meristem; no dedifferentiation is concerned. They are like the buds in the axils of leaves—traceable to the apical meristem of the stem through an uninterrupted sequence of meristematic cells, though surrounded by cells which mature and play their active parts in the life of the individual.

Roots, in general, do not do so well in this business as stems and leaves. They have no buds, of course, and so we should not expect them to respond so easily when cuttings are made; but why they should not dedifferentiate from their abundant parencyhma it is not easy to say. The best-known example of a plant that is propagated by root-cuttings is the sweet potato. Buds and roots are formed all over the surface of detached tubers or portions of tubers (presumably by dedifferentiation) and may be removed and planted out. Dahlia roots—tubers like those of the sweet potato—are also used in propagating; but in severing them from the parent plant one must be careful to include one of the buds which are already formed on the narrow neck where the tuber joins the stem. The buds come from the base of the stem rather than the root; the root is unable to form new buds, and propagation will be unsuccessful if these buds are lost.

So we use all parts of plants—all the so-called vegetative parts, the stems, leaves, and roots—in propagating the various species; obtaining the necessary new parts by the activity of persistent meristems or by dedifferentiation of various kinds of mature cells or by combinations of these two processes. Another sort of operation which makes use of the versatility of plant cells is grafting: the union of parts of two or more plants to make one. There are many methods of grafting and this is not the place to give the necessary practical directions. The essential thing in all methods is to bring living cells of the same kind in contact. The base of a small branch of an apple tree of some desired variety may be sharpened to two slanting faces which expose the tissues of wood and bark; and this branchlet is inserted in a slit in the cut end of a branch of a growing tree in such a way that the living parts of the bark and the cambiums of the two are in contact through at least part of their circumference. The joint is then sealed with wax. Food from the rooted plant, called the stock, can pass up into the grafted branchlet, called the cion; also water; and as the two continue their growth in thickness the new parts formed will be continuous across the union. The cion will, of course, if the graft "takes," continue its apical growth in the usual way, forming new stem and leaves, and ultimately flowers and fruit, as if it were still in its original place, served by its own stem and roots. The usual formation of callus will take place over exposed cut surfaces; and through the activities of the cambium within, the bark will become continuous over the joint.

Grafts may also be made by inserting an axillary bud cut out from one plant, with a bit of surrounding tissue, in a slit under the bark of a stock. Approach grafts are made by bringing two growing stems together side by side, with the rough parts of the bark shaved off. Grafts may be made between different species; even between different genera in the same family. So one species (or hybrid) of roses which forms the flowers we want is grafted on another species which forms a strong root system. In certain experimental studies—not made for horticultural purposes—tobacco has been grafted on potato and vice versa. Methods of union vary, the purposes vary; but the principle throughout is the same—to bring the living tissues of cion into contact with corresponding tissues of stock. From there on the meristems, and a few parenchyma cells, can take care of things.

PLANTS CAN PROPAGATE THEMSELVES

The sort of reproduction which uses only the roots, stems, and leaves of a plant (whether specially modified or not) is spoken of as vegetative reproduction; for the leaves, stems, and roots are called vegetative parts, meaning that they are primarily concerned with growth and feeding and absorption and transport. The vegetative parts are usually contrasted with flowers and fruit, which are more especially concerned with the next generation, and are generally called the reproductive parts. But in plants almost all parts *can* reproduce.

In the examples described above, vegetative reproduction is dependent upon human intervention, upon the severing of a stem, the detaching of a leaf or root, the keeping of such fragments at a suitable temperature and surrounded by a proper concentration of water. But vegetative reproduction occurs in nature also, without human aid, and very abundantly and variously.

Some of the plants which reproduce most easily by their vegetative parts are, naturally enough, among our most noxious weeds. Japanese honeysuckle, that pest of our southeastern coastal states (and not absent elsewhere), which clambers over trees and shrubs, stifling entire groves in its deadly embrace, owes its ubiquity partly to its powers of reproduction. Any bit of the creeping stem which is left in contact with the earth will live and grow. There is an abundance of buds in the axils of the numerous leaves (or where leaves once grew); and roots are easily formed—they normally arise from the nodes of the stem as it creeps over the ground. If any accident occurs to divide or break the stem, there will be that many more plants; our attempts at eradication with hoe or mattock usually serve mostly for propagation. Poison ivy (though it is spread by its berries) often owes its survival to similar habits of growth and reproduction. Such powers are really to be classed as being excessively vigorous growth. This emphasizes the close connection between growth and reproduction; for in such plants normal growth brings about reproduction by accident, as it were—if anything occurs to separate the new parts from the old.

In the majority of species vegetative reproduction is connected with the possession of special parts; those special kinds of roots, stems, and leaves, in fact, already described (p. 101) as packages of surplus food. Tubers, corms, bulbs, rhizomes are means of reproduction as well as reservoirs of food; the latter feature aiding the reproductive function. Still other parts—the runners of strawberries, for instance—are of special significance in reproduction even though they do not contain more than the usual amount of food.

A rhizome, as it grows, travels; for the growing end moves

—creeps—horizontally, and the other end gradually dies. Now and then—perhaps every spring, in such plants as Solomon's seal—the rhizome branches; there are now two growing ends advancing through the soil, in different directions. As the older part dies, the two branches are separated; the wave of decay that follows on the wave of growth finally reaches the point where the branches diverge. Even this is reproduction—there are two individuals now, not just one. This is a common feature of the growth of iris, of which the grower takes advantage when he digs and separates his clumps. It is also, unfortunately, a feature of many weeds. Quack grass, a pest of fields and gardens, has a creeping rhizome which is just as persistent and prolific as that of iris. The common fern called bracken, which may invade your garden, spreads and multiplies itself in the same way.

A potato is in a sense a rhizome—a horizontal underground stem; but it is also a tuber, an enlarged underground part filled with food. After the main stem of the parent plant has died and disintegrated, the shoots which sprout from the eyes of the tuber are on their own, as new individuals.

Strawberries—wild and cultivated—spread by runners, which are slender stems that "run" horizontally above the surface of the ground; they are also called stolons. The runner of a strawberry bears diminutive leaves which have buds in their axils; every other bud may grow, developing a stem and leaves like any bud; roots also develop from the same node. When the slim runner withers and dies, and these clusters of leaves and roots and a bit of stem are no longer connected with the parent, reproduction has occurred.

Many plants have stems which arch and touch earth again—almost like stolons. In fact one of the dogwoods receives its scientific name (*Cornus stolonifera*) because the tips of its branches strike root and may ultimately become separate plants; the branches are not true stolons, however, in spite of the name. The same sort of thing is seen in the brambles and briers—scrambling roses and blackberries and raspberries, which can form the sort of prickly jungle of arching and rooting stems that imprisoned the Sleeping Beauty. We take advantage of this ability to root at the tips by our practice of "layering," which is simply pegging the tip of a branch down to the earth so as to make sure of it.

All sorts of small wildings, the flowers of spring, have tubers or rhizomes that persist all winter—and all summer, too, for such plants are usually dormant then also—and help both to give the new growth a good start in spring and to form new plants: blood-root, trilliums, jack-in-the-pulpit, violets, and a host of others. Then there are the bulbs, those complex buds with flat stems and thick overlapping leaves full of food. Buds appear in the axils of these leaves too, and become new bulbs in their turn, which can lead their own individual lives as soon as the parent bulb is broken apart, whether by man or by nature. Sometimes new bulbs are formed outside the old one, at its base. Bulbs are characteristic of tulips, hyacinths, daffodils, onions, some lilies, and the wild flowers known as dog-tooth violets (which are related to lilies rather than to violets). These last, like tulips, form "droppers," in-genious branches that grow from the bases of leaves in the bulb; such a branch is a small hollow spear which grows straight down through the base of the bulb into the earth, *carrying within itself the bud in its axil*. In its new situation this bud forms a new bulb, below the old one; so the plant sends its offspring deeper and deeper into the earth. The bulbs of dog-tooth violets also send out long white branches horizontally; each can develop a new bulb at its tip. Tiger lilies and some others form small bulbs instead of ordinary buds in the axils of the leaves.

Many kinds of trees send up "suckers" from their roots. Beeches do this, and old apple trees. These new branches stand a good chance of becoming distinct plants if something happens to the parent or to the old roots that join them to the parent. Much the same is true of sumac. Nowadays we can eliminate such pests quite efficiently by spraying their leaves with one of the "hormonal" poisons (p. 23); before these were on the market, to get rid of a patch of sumac meant digging up all the earth in which it was growing and for some distance around, and carefully picking out every bit of root. Apparently (it has not yet been studied in detail) new buds may be formed from the parenchyma anywhere in this root. Not so large but equally hardy and troublesome is the little sorrel which was introduced from Europe late in the last century and spread rapidly across the United States. If you pull up the small plants carefully you will find many of them still connected by their roots. A small unfernlike fern called adder's-tongue spreads by its roots (probably far more readily than by its special reproductive parts); it has been found that the buds and new roots come from the apical meristem of the parent root (though they *may* also be formed from parenchyma).

That unwanted adornment of our lawns—fortunately very sensitive to spraying with 2,4-D—the common dandelion, has a particularly interesting main root. Many an old-time gardener can testify to the difficulty of getting all of it out of the ground; it always breaks off, and the lower part remains in the earth. Then the parenchyma cells of the phloem begin to proliferate, dividing to form an irregular projecting ring of parenchyma, a white and glistening mass of cells. In this ring dozens of buds are formed; new roots originate lower down in the old root and become connected with these buds; the result of any injury to the top of the old main root is a cluster of thrifty young plants in place of the old top.

Leaves, because of their lack of meristem, are not such frequent performers in the art of reproduction. But the pick-a-back plant gets its name from the little tuft of leaves which rides a mature leaf, springing from the base of the blade where it joins the leaf-stalk. These buds, like those of bryophyllum, came from the cells of the young leaf, when all were meristematic; they represent a persistent meristem. The roots develop by dedifferentiation of parenchyma, especially when leaves are detached and kept moist. Under such circumstances even a leaf which has no bud will form one, presumably by dedifferentiation.

Fern leaves, however, are somewhat more versatile than those of flowering plants; for they continue to grow for some time at their tips, like stems and roots. The tip of a fern leaf is coiled as it is formed; and within the coil, in the last turn, there is for a time an apical meristem. A small fern called the walking fern (it does not look much like a fern) illustrates this apical growth; for some of its leaves grow out into long threadlike tips. When the end of one of these touches moist earth or moss, new leaves and roots are soon seen; they are joined to the parent plant only by the whiplike leaf-end of the old leaf, which soon parts; and each such cluster of leaves and roots, attached to a minute stem-tip, becomes a new plant. Like the foliar embryo of bryophyllum, the future new plant was already formed in miniature in the apical meristem of the old leaf, which thus gives up its life to the next generation. Other ferns form small bulbs on their leaves, along the midrib; these are easily shaken off and will start life on their own if they find a spot of moist earth in which to grow.

PLANTS INHERIT

All these multifarious ways of forming new plants, of increasing the species, so characteristic of the plant world, illustrate over and over again the immense powers of growth resident in ordinary plants. It seems as if they could go on forever—forming new branches, new leaves, new roots.* Special reproductive parts, such as flowers, seem unnecessary; and in fact they are so in some very successful species; Japanese honeysuckle can form vast colonies without a single flower; certain aquatic plants, such as the tiny duckweed which floats by the million on quiet waters, flower only rarely but reproduce abundantly. And many domesticated plants— bananas, potatoes, sweet potatoes, pineapples—though they do flower, do not form fertile seeds, or do so only rarely.

These facts illustrate also the difficulty of drawing a line between growth and reproduction. The same things are going on in a stem-tip whether it is adding new parts to a plant or forming the parts of a new plant. It has even been suggested that all this so-called vegetative reproduction is actually nothing but growth: that all the potatoes in the world, for example, are really one vast plant. This seems far-fetched; but it does emphasize that nothing new occurs in reproduction of this kind as compared with growth— except that the new parts are somehow detached from the old and become independent of them.

* Whether or not old age in plants leads to changes which terminate growth and life is still controversial; but it is often said that plants are potentially immortal, growth and life being ended only by external factors.

One of the striking facts about all this sequence of events is that the kind of plant, the species, the variety, the race remains the same. We naturally expect all parts of one plant to be of the same species; but something is evidently carried over even into a new plant which holds it in the same course. The coleus cutting forms new leaves which are just like those of the parent plant (providing they grow in the same environment) and like all the other leaves of that variety; even the roots which bud out from the lower end of the cutting are unmistakably coleus roots. We use the word heredity to describe this phenomenon; just what does a new plant inherit? Obviously it receives from its parent the parts with which it begins its own development. A coleus cutting receives many cells from its parent: cells of the stem, of the buds, of a few mature leaves. A crassula may trace its inheritance to only a few epidermal cells of a leaf of its parent. The real question is not what it inherits from its parent, but what there is in this inheritance, these cells, that rules all further growth, so that as new leaves, for instance, are formed, they develop just the same marginal teeth, or just the same colors, or just the same smooth and succulent form, as those of the parent plant.

It is possible for a new plant to develop vegetatively from very few cells of the parent; even from one cell. In some species the new plants are formed from parenchyma cells; in others from meristematic cells; and in others (the majority) from both of these kinds of cells. What is there in such cells that is perpetuated during the development of the new parts and has to do with the kind of new parts that are formed—their size, shape, color, hairiness and so on? It must be something that persists unchanged through the divisions of cells, for all the new parts are made of cells formed by division. It must be something distributed equally to new cells formed by division, for one cell does not differ from its neighbors in its ability to produce a certain sort of leaf or root.

It will be recalled that every living cell consists of protoplasm (with or without a surrounding wall); and that the protoplasm (with a few exceptions which do not concern us here) is visibly divided into two parts, the more fluid cytoplasm, and a small body with a definite shape, the nucleus. The latter has not hitherto been considered in detail, though its general importance was suggested (p. 30). It contains a number of threadlike bodies called chromosomes.* In a cell that is not dividing, the chromosomes are difficult to distinguish; they are long, slender, variously coiled and tangled. There is also a body called a nucleolus ("little nucleus"). And all these things lie in a clear material called nuclear sap. But the chromosomes are the most important: *they control development.*

When the cell divides, the nucleus divides first; the nuclei of the new cells are formed directly from the nucleus of the parent cell. During the division of the nucleus the chromosomes undergo an extraordinary change. They shorten and thicken; they are now clearly visible (when stained with a suitable dye) in any good microscope. It may often be seen that there are characteristic differences among the chromosomes of one cell. Some are perhaps long, others much shorter; some may be marked by constrictions in definite places; some by "satellites"—small lumps attached to their ends by a slender connection. In short, these threads have individuality. Exactly the same chromosomes may be recognized in the other cells of the same plant; and in other plants of the same kind. There is a definite number of them, too; the number differing in different species. The cells of one kind of plant (or animal) possess a certain *set* of chromosomes, a definite number of certain definite kinds; just as a deck of cards is a set, a definite number of definite kinds of cards, each different from all the rest.

As the chromosomes become more easily visible, as their personalities emerge, the other parts of the nucleus suddenly vanish—nuclear membrane, nuclear sap, nucleolus; leaving the chromosomes lying in the middle of the cell, the sole representatives of the original nucleus. Each now becomes attached to two very delicate threads or fibers that extend the length of the cell, through the cytoplasm. The many fibers converge at each pole of the cell, forming a structure usually referred to as a spindle. At this time also careful examination discloses the remarkable fact that

---

* *Chromo-*, from the Greek, means "color"; *soma* in the same language means "body": "colored bodies." The name refers not to their natural color, for they have none; but to the readiness with which they take the stains used in preparing cells for microscopic study.

each chromosome is split lengthwise; a light streak may be seen down its entire length, and the ends of the two halves often diverge slightly.

What follows must almost be seen to be believed. It is as if the fine threads or fibers of the spindle, to which the chromosomes are attached, contract; and as if the result of this contraction is to tear the two halves of each chromosome apart, one towards one pole of the cell, the other towards the other. It is hard to understand the mechanics of this process; for the fibers have nothing visible to hold to at the other end from the chromosomes. Perhaps their "pulling" is wholly illusory, but the illusion is certainly striking; the half-chromosomes separate first at the points where they are attached to the fibers.

The result is that a group of half-chromosomes—or as we may now call them, "daughter" chromosomes—moves to each end of the cell; and there each group reorganizes itself into a complete nucleus, like the original nucleus except in size. A nuclear membrane reappears around each group of chromosomes, a nucleolus is formed within each membrane, and the chromosomes gradually lengthen into the thin, crooked, indistinct threads characteristic of the original nucleus. Furthermore, each of these daughter nuclei

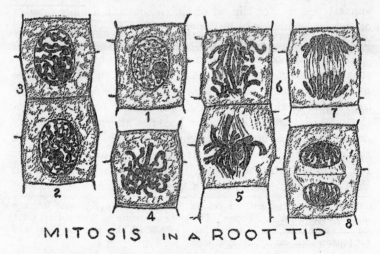

MITOSIS IN A ROOT TIP

contains a full set of chromosomes. Each received a half of every chromosome of the original set; and not merely one end or the other, but a half that has a sample of everything in the original thread from one end to the other.

And so it goes, division after division. Every new cell formed (in a meristem, for instance) receives a full set of chromosomes; and in turn bequeaths a full set to each of the cells which it forms. It is true there are irregularities; some cells come to possess several sets of chromosomes, more than their parents or neighbors; but only very rarely are such cells concerned with the formation of new parts (in growth or reproduction), so that such a condition is limited to certain parts of the plant; and almost never do cells survive and multiply with *less than one set*. In general we may say that all cells of a given species are alike in their chromosomes.

The name of the remarkable process of division which is responsible for this state of things is mitosis.* It has long excited the admiration of biologists and of amateurs, of all who have had an opportunity of seeing the chromosomes and following their history. Early students were quick to grasp the meaning implied by such a series of events. Here are the bodies demanded by a theory of heredity: bodies which are permanent from one generation to the next, and equally divided between the new cells formed. Nothing else in the cell—nothing visible, that is—shares these attributes. The chromosomes must therefore (they argued) be responsible for the development of the characteristics of the species or variety: they make heredity possible. Furthermore, since it is apparently important that the *entire length* of the chromosome be perpetuated, it is probable (they said) that there are in it important units arranged in a series lengthwise, units essential to development.

The science of experimental breeding, or genetics—the Gargantua of the biological sciences—has reinforced these deductions in a startling way. The evidence must be here deferred until the course of reproduction in flowers has been followed. But it may now be stated that there are units which control the development of particular bodily parts and characters, and that these units

---

* From a Greek word meaning "thread," in reference to the chromosomes.

are in the chromosomes, arranged more or less in a row down their length. To these units the name genes has been given.* Strange to say, we do not yet know *what* the genes are (though there are certain recent indications of their chemical nature); but we do know *where* they are. They have not been seen; but the evidence for their existence and situation leaves little room for doubt. Each gene is concerned in certain particular processes of development—we do not know how; if a gene is lacking or changed, development will follow a different course, so that perhaps the color of the leaves, or their size, or their hairiness will be different. We can even label certain genes, assigning to them letters and numbers, and state with entire confidence at what point on the visible chromosome each invisible unit is situated.† Since mitosis guarantees that each new cell shall receive a complete set of chromosomes and therefore *a complete set of genes*, it is easy to see why the new potato plant or rosebush or coleus cutting or apple cion should exactly resemble the parent from which it grew (except, of course, as changes in the environment may cause differences). The clue to the usefulness of vegetative propagation in horticulture and agriculture is the lengthwise division and equal distribution of the chromosomes of the nucleus.‡

The genes are remarkably constant; indeed that is one of the puzzling things about them, considering the work they do. But sometimes they do change; mutate, as we say. When a gene changes in some cell of a meristem, then all the cells descended from that

---

* They have also been called factors and determiners. *Gene* is from a Greek word signifying "origin."

† Much as the chemist talks about the arrangement of atoms in a molecule, or the physicist about the arrangement of electrons in an atom.

‡ The chromosomes, and the genes, are often spoken of (even by biologists) as the "bearers of heredity" or as "transmitting characters from parent to off-spring"; these figures of speech are both misleading and essentially meaningless. "Heredity" refers to a likeness between related plants. One cannot "carry" or "transmit" heredity or hereditary characters from one plant to another, except in an abstract sense; the actual likeness between them depends on their growth. There are no colors of leaves or sizes or shapes of leaves or hairs in the chromosomes or elsewhere in the cells with which plants begin their lives. These characteristics are the results of development. The *genes control development*; and it is because parent and offspring contain the same genes that they are alike.

aberrant cell will possess the changed gene; and this may have an effect on all the parts which can be traced to that cell as an ancestor. Perhaps the gene is one of those that are concerned in the formation of chlorophyll, and the change that occurs, the mutation, will interfere with that process so that that particular series of cells will lack the capacity to be green. So we may get leaves with white or yellow stripes (as wandering jew) or a white or yellow margin (variegated geranium or ivy). Or an entire branch may lack chlorophyll. Such conditions can be perpetuated as long as we use the parts thus affected in the production of each new generation; relying on an indefinite series of mitoses to carry on the lineages of cells. In this way we may get a new variety, sometimes called a "sport" or a "mutant." Sometimes also one of those aberrations of mitosis already mentioned will affect cells perpetuated by reproduction, so that the new plants have three or four sets of chromosomes, or even more. This also results in a new race, which may or may not breed true. The use of X-rays and of such drugs as colchicine stimulates the production of new kinds of plants by such changes in the inheritance.

The poets of ancient Greece told of a mythical monster named the chimaera,* which had the head of a lion, the body of a wild goat, and the tail of a serpent—and perhaps a few other mismated parts. We apply the same name to any plant or animal which contains in its one body tissues which differ genetically; in short to a certain sort of freak. The variegated plants whose differently colored parts have different genes are chimaeras.†

Chimaeras may originate at the junction of cion and stock in a graft; the two different kinds of tissues overlapping, as it were, and both continuing growth as parts of the same organ. Chimaeras may also be brought about artificially, like the "sports" mentioned above. In this way it has been possible to produce a

---

* The word actually meant a "she-goat."

† Some variegation, however, is due to the behavior of one gene or group of genes which is present in all the cells but acts in different ways in different cells; this sort of thing causes the patterns of color, for instance, in a flower, and the red striping in certain kinds of corn. Plants with this type of variegation are not chimaeras. Still other types of variegation, as in tulip, camellia, and abutilon, are caused by a virus and may be classed as a disease.

different chromosomal condition in the outer layer of a meristem, the inner cells remaining unchanged (or vice versa); so that the parts of leaves, flowers, and fruit which are formed by the outer cells are different from the remaining parts of these organs.

Formerly it was believed that the grafting of two different kinds of plants was equivalent to an actual hybridization; that the stock contributed something besides nutriment to the cion, so that the seeds formed on the latter would have something of both stock and cion in their inheritance. This belief antedated our present knowledge of the existence and behavior of genes. We know of no way in which genes (or any other parts of the cell) could migrate from the graft-union up through the tissues of the cion and into the developing seed. Careful experiments have demonstrated that the cion bequeaths only its own inheritance to its offspring and receives nothing but nourishment from the stock. There is really no such thing as a "graft-hybrid"—unless we use this term to refer to the chimaeras mentioned above.

Genes are so wonderful that we have become somewhat infatuated with them. Rarely in the history of science has such a sound and imposing edifice of knowledge been raised in so short a time as that which constitutes the science of genetics. So vast is our knowledge of the behavior of chromosomes and their contained genes, of their effects, of their aberrancies and mutabilities, that we sometimes forget how little we know of the genes themselves and of how they bring about their contribution to development. Furthermore, we tend to forget the rest of the cell, the cytoplasm. *This also is inherited.* It is true that the cell makes no effort to divide the cytoplasm equally between its daughter cells. But there are in it some more or less permanent bodies which divide and pass into the daughter cells much as chromosomes do. This is true of the chloroplasts; these (or their rudiments) are inherited by the new cells intact; and some types of variegation in leaves have been traced to cytoplasmic inheritance. In this department of genetics we are perhaps standing just at the threshold of new knowledge.

7

Flowers

WHAT MAKES PLANTS FLOWER?

Birds put on their brightest plumage and sing their loudest in the spring of the year, in that period of movement and growth. This is their time of mating. Later, as the days grow longer, they are busy with domestic cares; their voices are hushed, their bright plumage shed. Their brief reproductive season corresponds with the first burst of bloom that adorns the earth: crocuses and daffodils in our gardens, violets and mayflowers in the woodlands. Is there any connection? Do flowers also have a "mating season" and is it related to seasonal factors?

It is true that flowers are reproductive parts; but not all plants flower in the spring. Some, indeed, bloom throughout the growing season: many roses are more or less continuously in flower from early June to October; and so, unfortunately, are dandelions and other unwanted things. But it is equally evident that most flowers have their seasons. Our shrubberies—forsythia and weigela and the rest—flower in the spring and show no color but green the rest of the season. They are followed by magnolia, apple blossom, dogwood, cherries, in their appointed times. Summer comes in with iris and peonies, and later brings delphinium and phlox and zinnia and petunia; and the corn tassels out. Finally asters and goldenrod and chrysanthemums bring the chapter to its close.

What makes a plant flower? Is it merely a matter of age? Does it reach a certain size and then flower? Or are there factors in its surroundings which govern its development? Evidently it is not easy to make a general statement. Asters and most chrysanthemums flower only in the fall, with cocklebur and ragweed. You can grow them to full size in the summer, but they do not flower then. What is the difference between summer and fall?

The answer is not a simple one. There are many differences: the days are longer and the nights shorter in summer, the sunlight is brighter, temperatures are higher, in some places water may be more or less abundant. Only a few years ago two botanists of the United States Department of Agriculture, W. W. Garner and H. A. Allard, singled out one of these varying factors and showed that it had a decisive effect on the flowering of many species: the length of the day.*

In spring, when the hours of daylight are few (and the hours of darkness many), violets flower, and forsythia, and a little later, strawberries; they will bloom again, if the frosts hold off, in the autumn, when the days have shrunk again to the same length as in spring. Cosmos, ragweed, cocklebur likewise flower in the fall when the days are short; being annual, they could not flower in the spring. Poinsettia flowers, under glass, appear in the middle of winter. But any of these can be induced to flower in midsummer *if they are covered during a part of every day*—i.e. if the short days and long nights are brought about artificially.

Many other plants flower only during the long days of summer: spinach, for instance, and beets, lettuce, most of the cereal grains, the hay plants timothy and clover, potatoes, gladiolus. And these can be brought into flower in midwinter, under glass of course, merely by adding some hours of artificial illumination to the hours of daylight. For it is not the intensity of the light—it is the number of hours of light that is decisive; and a weak light (if not *too* weak) can be substituted for some of the hours of daylight.

Other plants, again, are unaffected by the length of day: they flower when they are fully grown, and keep on flowering indefinitely without regard to the changing hours of daylight, as

---

* Generally known to botanists as the photoperiod; the phenomenon described in these pages is called photoperiodism. It had been noticed before Garner and Allard; but its significance was not grasped.

long as the other factors of the environment permit. Some of these indifferent plants are tomatoes, zinnias, dandelion, cotton, buckwheat, many varieties of tobacco, many roses.

From the foregoing it is quite clear that the mere length of day does exert a controlling influence on the flowering of many species. (It is also a controlling factor in the singing and in the migration of birds.) We can classify flowering plants on this basis in three groups: short-day plants (SDP), long-day plants (LDP), and indifferent plants.

Just what the mechanism is, just how the hours of light and darkness exert their influence is not yet known. Extensive researches have been made and are being made in an effort to clear this up. It has been shown that the effect is "perceived" in the leaves; defoliated plants do not respond in the same way. It is known also that short-day plants *need the long dark period*; they might as well be called long-night plants; for when the long period of darkness is interrupted even for a few seconds by bright light, the impulse towards flowering also is interrupted—the plants remain in the vegetative condition. Long-day plants, on the other hand, can flower under continuous illumination; they do not need any dark period. A long dark period *prevents* them from forming flowers: so that these plants might almost better be called short-night plants. *Both groups need a period of light* for flowering as for their general welfare; something is formed in the light which makes for flowering.

A cocklebur plant (SDP) was grown in summer (long days) with two principal stems. One of these was covered a part of every day: its days were shortened, its nights lengthened. Naturally this branch flowered; *so did the other*. The conclusion was drawn that something is formed in the branch subjected to short days, something which makes for flowering; and that this something passes from one part of the plant to another (even from one plant to another if the two are united by an approach graft). One thinks at once of a hormone, a growth substance; and it was proposed that plants form a flower-inducing substance. This was even given a name: florigen. It is true that the above experiment did not work with other short-day plants. When Biloxi soybeans were treated, only the covered branch flowered. But if the leaves were removed from the other branch, then it too flowered. Florigen—or whatever causes this—was powerless in the presence of the leaves. The leaves are apparently necessary, in the normal course of things, to the formation of flowers; they "perceive" the length of day. May they also prevent flowering? Some researchers think that flowering depends on a balance between two things produced by the leaves. So we wander in a maze of conflicting data and conclusions.

The problems are tantalizing. Why should there be three groups of plants with different ways of forming flowers? Why should some need a long period of darkness to flower while others are prevented from flowering by a long period of darkness? The answers are still in the future. Florigen? No one has succeeded in extracting it or isolating it or doing anything at all that would give positive evidence of its existence. Perhaps it does exist; but very painstaking search has failed to reveal it. Meanwhile it has a name.

And meanwhile the plain facts of the dependence of flowering upon the length of day are of considerable value to the grower of plants. Chrysanthemums can now be easily grown and brought into flower in midsummer. Gladiolus can be flowered in midwinter. By simply devising a means of darkening the benches or beds for a part of every day, or a means of adding extra hours of light by electric lamps, the flower grower can put his wares on the market at any time of year, whenever he wants to; whenever people want the flowers.

This relation between the hours of daylight and the formation of flowers is so clear, so striking, so susceptible to experimentation, and so useful to the plant grower that its appeal to the botanical imagination is not surprising. Botanists are like other people—they are often influenced by fashion. It must be emphasized that the length of day is not the only factor of the environment that influences flowering. There is also—to name but the most obvious —temperature. In general, a rise in temperature, within certain limits, causes an increase in the rate of physical and chemical events, within plants as well as without. So at certain temperatures the production of foods or hormones or other substances is more rapid than at others. It is no cause for surprise, therefore, that the development of flowers, which seems to depend on various things produced in the light and sometimes perhaps on things formed in the dark, should be affected by temperature as well as by light. Strawberry plants behave usually as short-day plants; if the temperature is kept low, they will go on flowering even into the summer.

Another example of the effects of temperature is the practice known as vernalization.* Winter wheat is known for its late flowering; if it is sown in the spring, it will often fail to form ears before the end of the season. But it has been found that if the soaked or sprouted grains are chilled to a temperature near freezing for a few weeks, the plants will flower—"head out"— much earlier. The same thing is true of other grains, and of plants in other families (e.g. sugar beet). This may have practical usefulness in certain climates where the growing season is very short. Under such conditions methods have been worked out for treating seeds in quantity. There have been claims for increased yield. But in most parts of the world vernalization seems to be mainly of scientific interest. The physiology of the phenomenon is not yet understood.

In any discussion of the causes of flowering, there is a more or less tacit assumption that flowering and vegetative growth are opposed: if one is favored, the other is correspondingly suppressed; if a plant grows rapidly and forms many stems and leaves its flowering is likely to be delayed; if it flowers profusely, vegetative growth is slowed or even ended. There is certainly some truth in this. The annuals and biennials in our gardens—zinnias, lupine, cabbage, lettuce—grow vigorously at first with no sign of a flowering stalk; when they flower, they have finished their growth, except perhaps for the production of additional flower-stalks below the terminal one. Some of them grow during one season, flower the next. The same is true of the annual shoots of perennial plants— phlox, sunflowers, hardy asters. But there are many exceptions,

---

* "Vernal" means "concerned with spring"; vernalization means something like "placed in a spring-time state." It is called *yarovizatsia* in Russia, *printanisation* in France—the meaning being just the same, since these also are derived from words for "spring."

many plants that continue to bloom and grow at once, such as many kinds of roses. We must be cautious about speaking of the contrast between flowering and vegetative activity, especially since the causes of both, the factors that differentiate them, are so complex and as yet so imperfectly understood.

Certain classic experiments with tomatoes were performed by E. J. Kraus and H. R. Kraybill. They indicated that when all nutrients are abundant but nitrogen is in excess as compared with the carbohydrates present in the plant, growth is vigorous and flowering more or less suppressed; while an abundance of carbohydrates (formed by the leaves under bright illumination) as compared with the nitrogen (but this not lacking) makes for a plant which grows and flowers. The significance of these facts is not yet wholly understood; nutrition is a complex subject and there are many more factors in flowering than the balance between nitrogen and carbohydrates. However, it does seem to be true that limitation of the supply of nitrogen, provided the plant is otherwise well nourished, tends towards earlier flowering, at least in some species; and an excess of nitrogenous fertilizer may retard flowering.

THE ARRANGEMENT OF FLOWERS

It is true, *as far as one stem-tip is concerned*, that flowering is opposed to growth; it ends it. Every flower is formed from an apical meristem. It begins as a bud—an apical meristem covered by the beginnings of leaves; but the leaves are the parts of the flower. The stem-tip ceases to form more parts after a certain number (a more or less definite number) have been formed; and it does not elongate and separate these floral leaves—instead they remain closely bunched. The change from one sort of activity to the other in the stem-tip is quite sudden and decisive. The meristem was forming leaves; now it forms flower-parts. From similar beginnings the visible result is quite different.

Every flower, then, is formed *at the end of a stem*. In some kinds of plants this is the whole story. A magnolia has flowers at the ends of its branches, one flower to a branch. Below the flowers leaves and branches arise, from lateral buds. A crocus flowers in the same way; and there are many others.* But flowers much more usually grow in a bouquet, in what is technically called an inflorescence; a cluster of flowers in which all the branches are devoted to flowering and bear no leaves of the ordinary kind. An inflorescence may consist of two or three flowers or of hundreds. A stalk of sweet peas illustrates one extreme, a flowering branch of lilac the other.

The stem which bears a rose at its tip may form, a short distance below the flower, two narrow, pointed objects somewhat resembling very small leaves; one usually a short distance above the other. From the axil of each of these a flower may grow—blooming usually a little later than the terminal flower. This is a simple three-flowered inflorescence known technically as a dichasium;† a type of inflorescence of which many of the more elaborate and larger kinds are built. Simple dichasia composed of three flowers are not easy to find in nature or in the garden. The lateral flowers themselves bear small leaflike scales on their stalks, like those from whose axils they spring; and from these yet other flowers may spring, so that the cluster has seven flowers instead of three. If this happens yet again—if each lateral flower again forms two lateral flowers in the axils of the scales on its stalk—then the inflorescence will be composed of fifteen flowers. And so on. This is the sort of thing we see in a flowering branch of bryophyllum or of begonia or of snow-in-summer. Usually, however, there are irregularities in the pattern of branching. Some lateral flowers fail to develop, so that one flower-stalk will bear a branch from only *one* of its scales. Or the terminal flower will abort, only the lateral ones reaching maturity, so that the stem seems to fork where the two branches arise.

Many kinds of plants form large clusters of hundreds of flowers built up in the way just described—dichasium upon dichasium; with, however, many irregularities, so that the pattern may be

---

* One is tempted to add the dandelion as an example. But the "flower" of this familiar weed is not a flower; it is really a group of many small flowers; see p. 164. A similar statement may be made of flowering dogwood.

† From the Greek word *dichasis*, "division"; because the stem seems to divide or fork below the terminal flower. Notice that the *ch* in words derived from Greek is pronounced as in "architect."

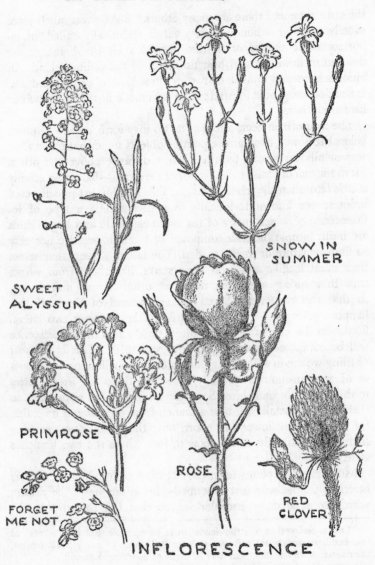

SNOW IN
SUMMER

SWEET
ALYSSUM

PRIMROSE

ROSE

RED
CLOVER

FORGET
ME NOT

INFLORESCENCE

difficult to trace. Such inflorescences may be flat; look at that of an elderberry or a viburnum. These are known as cymes.*

Besides such large and rather loosely planned inflorescences there are a number in which the dichasial plan is more exactly followed, though variously modified. The description and naming of these types become technical; here we need only mention some of the more common. Of these perhaps the most familiar is the inflorescence of the household geranium or pelargonium. The structure of this may be understood by imagining that the part of every flower-stalk *below* the two lateral branches is shortened, so that all the flowers seem to arise from the same point on the main stem. This is called an umbel.† The same sort of cluster is found growing from an onion plant and on a milkweed. If you imagine the *upper* part of every flower-stalk *also* contracted, you have the close cluster of small flowers seen on the flowering dogwood; each cluster, known as a head, surrounded by four large petal-like bud-scales. It is interesting to study this inflorescence as it opens and to notice that to one side and the other of each open flower is an unopened bud; the three form a dichasium, of which there are many in the head.

A very curious and quite common type of inflorescence is to be seen in forget-me-not and sedum and tobacco and spring beauty. It starts with a dichasium, but only one lateral flower appears—say the left-hand one. This forms its terminal flower and, again, only one lateral—this time on the right hand. Growth continues in this way, in zig-zag fashion, each branch springing from the side of the preceding one. The whole inflorescence may coil at its tip like the tail of a scorpion.

If you look at the flowers of a mint, you will find them growing in small tight clusters in the axils of the paired leaves. The flowers are in close-packed groups on the dichasial plan; all together they compose a larger inflorescence, the youngest part of which is at

---

* From a Greek word which has the general significance of "something swollen"; its botanical application being arbitrary. The word is also used for the whole group of inflorescences on the dichasial plan, from a simple three-flowered dichasium up; they are all spoken of as cymose.

† From the Latin *umbella*, "shade"; because the flower-stalks radiate like the ribs of a sunshade or umbrella.

the top (since that is where the stem is youngest). Suppose this is simplified by reducing each little axillary cluster to a single flower; then we have what is called a raceme. It differs from the cyme in having a number of lateral branches (instead of just two) and in flowering usually *from the base up*—towards the growing point of the main stem, which may or may not continue to add to the stem and to form flowers after the lowest have shed their petals and formed their fruits. The raceme is quite common: a snap-dragon is one example, sweet alyssum another.

If we imagine that the main stem of a raceme fails to elongate, but continues to form its axillary flowers, all the flower-stalks will spring from almost the same point; this is what we see on a primrose. This also is an umbel; it resembles what we have already found on an onion or a geranium, although it is formed in a different way. In the umbel of an onion or geranium or milkweed there is a series of branches one on another, each arising very near the base of the preceding; in a primrose the branches all spring from one main stem, which is very short. In the umbels of geraniums and milkweeds, some of the outermost flowers will be the last to open; in the umbel of a primrose the central flower is the one nearest the tip of the main stem and is the last to open. One entire large family is called the umbel-bearers (Umbelliferae), because practically all its species have flowers in umbels: carrots, parsnips, parsley, celery, anise, dill, all these are in the family; besides the extremely poisonous weeds cowbane and hemlock.* Most of their umbels are compound; i.e. each branch has a small umbel at its tip instead of one flower.

A further development of the same scheme is what we see in clover: the flowers on very short stalks, grouped as in an umbel, but in a very compact bunch. This is a head; which, like an umbel, can be formed in various ways: the head of clover is a contracted raceme, while the head of flowering dogwood is a contracted compound dichasium.

More or less related to the raceme family of inflorescences (spoken of collectively as racemose), but often rather mixed in their origins, are several rather vaguely defined types of flower-

---

* Not to be confused with the evergreen tree of the same name.

groups. The sort of loose, much-branched arrangement we see in so many grasses—fescue and bluegrass and oats and redtop—is called a panicle. The tighter groups characteristic of foxtail grass or orchard grass or wheat or rye are called spikes. The inflorescence of smartweed is a spike, too. Maize has two kinds of inflorescences: the tassel is a panicle, the ear a spike.

Which brings us to the question (which perhaps we should have considered before this): what is a flower? Are flowers found on corn and oats as well as on rosebushes? Does one plant sometimes have two kinds of flowers? How does a flower form fruit, and what is fruit?

THE ESSENTIAL PARTS

Part of the fascination of flowers is their infinite variety. Perhaps we think first of the showy flowers—iris, daffodils, lilies, roses, dahlias, orchids: flaunting their many lovely colors, their delicate perfumes, their graceful forms. But there are flowers which have no such attractions, which are minute, scarcely to be seen without a magnifier. Grasses and sedges and rushes have flowers, and oaks and elms and alders and willows, and duckweed; and all these form fruit, too. There are also the unattractive little greenish flowers of ragweed, responsible for much human suffering. There are flowers that smell like a skunk, and others with the odor of putrid flesh. Yet all these various things are alike in plan: they all have the same parts, in spite of all the differences in size, shape, color, odor. They are all alike also in their essential functions: they all perpetuate their species, they all form fruits which contain seeds, and they all form these things in much the same way. The only exceptions to this statement are some of the things we have bred for our gardens, which are for show only and of no use to the plants which bear them: most peonies, dahlias, flowering cherries, and others. These are propagated by their vegetative parts.

In external form and appearance flowers are certainly so various that it is difficult to know how to begin a description of them, to find a formula which will fit them all. Most flowers are small, too small for a beginning study. For first inquiry it is best to choose the largest flower that we can find: say a magnolia. We enjoy these for the beautiful display they make in the spring, mantling their trees with pink and white petals; we need no botanical instruction to know that much. But what the botanist knows as the "essential" parts of the flower play a small part in this brilliant and lovely exhibition. If you look more closely than usual at a single magnolia flower, you will see in the center of it a sort of column; its base is surrounded by many narrow spreading things tinged with red or gold; its upper part is covered with small, curved, greenish projections; *these* are the essential parts, the reproductive parts, the parts that give the flower meaning in the economy of the species.

The spreading things at the base of the column, shaped like short ribbons or straps, are the stamens.* Since the time of

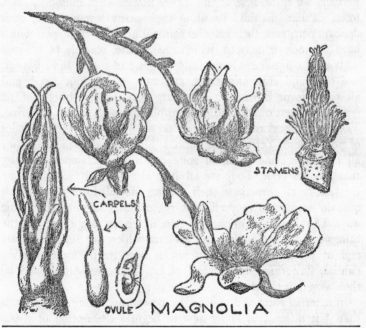

STAMENS

CARPELS

OVULE MAGNOLIA

---

* From a Greek word meaning "hair" or "thread"; those of most flowers have thread-like stalks.

Linnaeus these have been recognized as the male parts of the plant; though they cannot be strictly compared with any parts of animals. They form pollen, a fine dust.* This is the fertilizing agent; but it is not the same as the animal sperm.

The stamens spring from the base of the central column of the flower. On its upper part, close-packed, are borne the female parts, named carpels.† Each carpel is shaped rather like a long tear-drop, with the narrow upper end bent. The lower, larger end contains in an interior cavity a minute body, or two: the future seeds. The early botanists, who were too anxious to find in plants the same female parts as they recognized in animals, called the lower part of the carpel the ovary and the rudimentary seed within it the ovule. The comparison was a mistaken one, for the ovule is not, as the name would indicate, a small egg; nor does any part of the carpel correspond to the ovary of an animal; but the names have stuck. The slender part of the carpel above the ovary bears aloft a small sticky part which catches and holds the fertilizing dust, the pollen. The slender part is the style, the receptive region the stigma.‡ In a magnolia flower the two are not clearly separate; the stigma extends down one side of the style. In other flowers the stigma is a more definite part carried at the extreme tip of the style.

These parts are surrounded by the beautifully colored and often fragrant leaves generally known as petals. There are two circles, or whorls, of these; the botanist restricts the use of the word petal to the inner whorl, calling the outer whorl sepals; although they all look alike. If we are impatient of such distinctions, we can use the word perianth⁋ for all of them together. All the parts of the flower are attached to that central axis already noticed: the perianth at its base, where it is thickest; the stamens just above the perianth, in a spiral arrangement; and the carpels

---

* That is the literal meaning of the Greek word: "dust."

† From *karpos*, Greek, meaning "fruit"; as will be seen, the matured carpel is the nucleus of the fruit.

‡ "Style" is from a word meaning "column." The Greek word *stigma* means literally "mark," "brand."

⁋ *Peri-* in Greek means "around," as in "periphery," "perimeter"; *anthos* means "flower" (compare "anthology"); so "perianth" means "around the flower"; the outer part of the flower.

on the rest, also arranged in a spiral. The axis is the end of the stem which bears the flower; it is termed the receptacle.

Such is the fundamental plan of a flower: a receptacle which bears a perianth, stamens, and carpels. One or more of these parts may be lacking; other parts may be present. But whatever the flower, whatever its complexity and superficial peculiarities, the parts that are present bear the same relation to each other as in a magnolia: carpels on the apex of the receptacle, in the center of the flower; stamens below or around the carpels; and perianth around them in turn.

The functioning of these parts may be briefly outlined here, and dealt with more fully in the following pages. The pollen is carried by wind, insects, or other agents to the stigma. Here it sends forth long, living threads—the pollen tubes—which penetrate the style and reach the ovary, fertilizing the ovules. The ovary becomes the fruit, or at least the essential part of the fruit; the ovules develop into the seeds. The perianth plays some part, usually, in the distribution of the pollen, and then withers away and is lost. The fruit splits open, or is eaten by animals, or is wafted away on the breeze; in one way or another it delivers its freight of seeds to the earth which awaits them; they germinate, and a new generation—of magnolias or maples or apples or beans— is launched.

LILIES AND ROSES

Even casual examination of a magnolia flower (particularly if it is split lengthwise through its middle) reveals an arrangement of parts which recalls that of a leaf-bud at the tip of a growing stem. A leaf-bud consists of a stem-tip crowned by a cluster of closely overlapping leaves. This, in fact, is also the classical concept of a flower; the floral parts are considered to be leaves, of different kinds. It is not difficult to compare the perianth with leaves; its parts are shaped, if not always colored, like leaves. The stamens and carpels are less leaflike in appearance; but there are reasons* for regarding them also as leaves. The central axis,

---

* Unfortunately not regarded as conclusive by all botanists; this subject is still somewhat controversial.

the receptacle, has the internal structure of a stem; there is no doubt of its identity; and it forms the flower-parts in much the same way as an ordinary stem forms its leaves, at its growing tip. The striking difference between a flower-bud and a leaf-bud is that the latter normally continues to grow longer, while a flower-bud does not—it all matures in the act of forming the floral parts and there is no part left to prolong the growth of the stem.* The floral "leaves" remain bunched at the tip of the stem, where they are formed; not scattered along the side of a branch, as foliage leaves are.

If you have no magnolia at hand but do have a lily or an apple blossom or a rose or a daffodil or a crocus or a skunk cabbage or a tomato flower or a dahlia or a dandelion—you will be at first puzzled at not finding an arrangement like that described in the preceding pages. *Actually the plan of these various flowers is the same,* even though it cannot be discerned at first sight. The colored petals are present in most of them; there is certainly a perianth; but the stamens and carpels are not on a projecting axis in the center.

The sort of flower we see on a magnolia, generally considered by botanists an ancient type, the sort of flower from which others have been evolved, is not very common. It is seen also in a buttercup (the wild kind, not the "double" flower of the garden) and in an anemone. The curious little wild flower called mousetail has an even longer receptacle—a long scaly tail arising from a circle of tiny petals. But the great majority of flowers have a short, flat receptacle, with all the floral parts arising at about the same level. And many have a cup-shaped receptacle—hollowed out instead of projecting—with carpels in the center of the cup, other parts on the rim. Moreover in most flowers the parts are less numerous than in a magnolia, and arranged in circles or whorls instead of in a spiral.

Consider a lily. One of the obvious things about it is that there are just six parts to the perianth, three outer and three inner†; and six stamens. Not only are the parts less numerous than in a

---

* Except for some freaks, in which a tuft of green leaves grows from the center of the flower.

† The three outer ones may be likened to sepals, the three inner to petals; but since they are all colored and shaped alike, or nearly so, this distinction is not usually made.

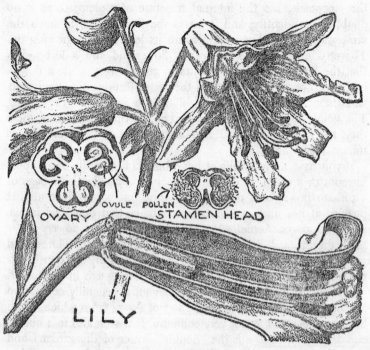

OVARY · OVULE · POLLEN · STAMEN HEAD

LILY

magnolia or a buttercup flower; they are fixed in number. In the middle, surrounded by the stamens, is what looks like a single large carpel: much larger than a carpel of magnolia, but having the same general outline—ovary at the base, style and stigma above. If you cut across this ovary you will find not one internal cavity but three; each containing the rudiments of many seeds. This thing in the center of the flower is actually made of *three carpels united* side by side. Another indication of its compound nature is seen in the stigma, which has three lobes.

Long ago, before botanists had any very clear idea of the structure or functions of a flower, they devised more or less fanciful names for the parts which they saw. This thing in the middle they called a pestle, because it resembles in shape the implement with which a chemist compounds medicines and other mixtures in his mortar. The Latin form of this word is *pistillum*; and, since learned people wrote and spoke in Latin, this form, slightly modified, has come down to us as the name of the part in question: we call it a pistil. This name is applied regardless of whether the body is made of a single carpel or of several united, and whether there are many such bodies or only one. A pistil is simply a body formed of an ovary containing an ovule or ovules and surmounted by a style and stigma.* A magnolia or buttercup or columbine has many *simple* pistils, each formed of one carpel. A cherry or sweet pea has one simple pistil. A simple pistil is the same as a carpel. A lily has a *compound* pistil, formed of three carpels joined. The pistil of a snapdragon has two carpels, that of a geranium five. But simple pistils and compound pistils have much the same external shape.

All the parts of a lily flower arise from a small flat surface, the slightly expanded end of the stem; this is the receptacle.

In Christian symbolism the lily has always represented chastity. The blood of martyrdom was represented by the rose. "These two noble flowers" (as one old poet has it) were so associated in religious ritual and art that to speak of one was to call the other to mind; and—such is the force of our traditions—this is still true.

A rose resembles a magnolia or buttercup in having large indefinite numbers of stamens and carpels, the latter forming many simple pistils. But the receptacle, the end of the stem, is expanded and hollowed out; it is like a cup or urn.† The interior is lined with many small downy pistils, their styles rising enough so that their stigmas project through the opening of the cup—and often fill it. Stamens stand around the rim, a crowd of them. There are

---

* The style is lacking in some flowers; in a tulip the stigma is seated on the summit of the ovary.

† Recent researches indicate that this cup, which is better termed the hypanthium (meaning literally "under the flower"), is at least in many flowers formed of the basal parts of perianth and stamens, all grown together; rather than of the end of the stem to which all these are attached. It does not greatly matter; the point is that growth from the tip of the stem takes this form —it rises in a ring below the apex instead of in a column at the apex. There is reason to think that in a rose the structure is partly stem and partly the united bases of the floral leaves. For the purposes of elementary discussion the term receptacle may be used to designate the structure from which the parts of the flower *seem* to spring, whatever its true morphological nature.

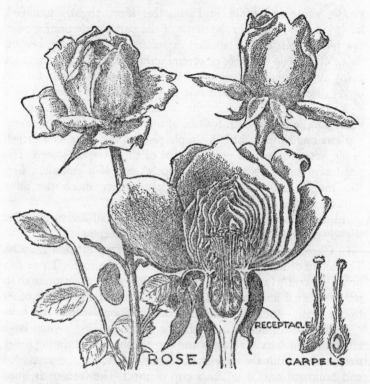

usually, in the wild roses, five petals and five sepals, all composing the perianth; here we have a clear distinction between the fragrant and brilliant petals and the green, more or less leaflike sepals. The petals of any flower are collectively known as the corolla, the "little crown"; and the sepals as the calyx, the "covering."

The roses of our gardens illustrate one way in which flowers have become "double." The extra whorls of petals arise on the rim of the receptacle at the expense of the stamens; there is reason to think that even the petals normally present in the wild species are transformed, sterilized stamens.

A further development of the receptacle, and a puzzling one, is to be seen in an apple blossom. It is cup-shaped or vase-shaped, as in a rose. It contains only five carpels, more or less joined in the

OVARY IN RECEPTACLE

APPLE

center to form a compound pistil (the styles, however, are mostly separate; five styles, each with its stigma). But the sides of the carpels and the sides of the receptacle are joined, so that it is impossible to say where one begins and the other leaves off: *receptacle and carpels form one solid structure.* It is this that later ripens into an apple, that fruit "with a good savour and merry" (as an old gardener wrote). The other parts of the flower seem to spring from the top of the ovary, just around the styles; for which reason the ovary is spoken of as "inferior" (below the other parts). In reality these parts grow from the receptacle which surrounds the ovary like an outer skin. All the other ovaries so far mentioned are "superior" ovaries—they are clearly situated on the extremity of the apex.*

---

* More technically, the type of flower formed on an apple tree is called epigynous (*epi*, Greek, meaning "upon"; *gyne*, also Greek, meaning "woman", "female"); what we have in a rose or cherry is perigynous (*peri*, "around"); and all other types are hypogynous (*hypo*, "under"). This is naming the types of flowers from the point of view of the stamens and perianth rather than that of the ovary. The ovary is superior or partly so in perigynous and hypogynous flowers, inferior in epigynous flowers.

THE VARIETY IN FLOWERS

Other parts of flowers besides carpels may be joined. Usually the sepals are joined to form a cup at the base of the petals; look at a sweet pea. The petals of many kinds together form a sort of bell or tube, at the summit of which their tips may separate, taking the form of teeth or lobes; you may see this in phlox or primrose or bluebell. In such flowers the stalks of the stamens are commonly joined to the petals for part of their length, so that the stamens seem to spring from points high on the inside of the petal-tube. In other flowers some or all of the stamens are joined by their stalks with each other, so as to form a cylinder around the pistil; in a sweet pea nine of the ten are so joined, the tenth (the uppermost) is free; in a hollyhock flower the numerous stamens are all united. In a sunflower or daisy the stamens are united by their heads (the pollen-bearing parts), their stalks being separate.

Magnolia flowers, lilies, daffodils, the flowers of phlox and primrose and hollyhock are radially symmetric as you look them in the face; sepals and petals of essentially the same size and shape radiate from the center. But this is not true of sweet peas and snapdragons and gladiolus and larkspur and violets and many others. In these flowers, as they face you, the upper parts of the perianth (and often the upper stamens) differ from the lower. Right and left halves are still alike, so that the flowers may be said to be bilaterally symmetric; symmetric with respect to a vertical line rather than a central point. In botanical manuals the radially symmetric flowers are spoken of as "regular," the others as "irregular."

The first generally adopted classification of flowering plants was that devised by the great Swedish botanist Carl Linnaeus in the 18th century. It was arbitrary, being based principally on the numbers of stamens and carpels. A hundred years later, when Charles Darwin was publishing his books, the idea was gaining acceptance that the multitudinous kinds of living things are descended from a smaller number of kinds, perhaps ultimately from a single remote ancestor, through changes in the stream of heredity. This notion is now widely held, and botanists try to

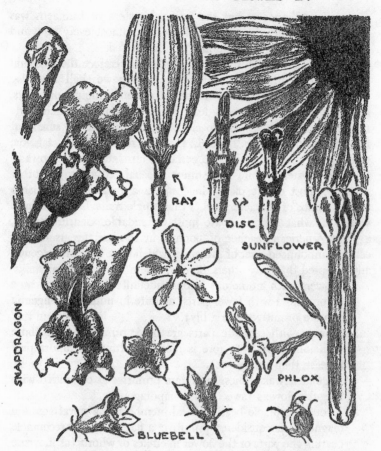

RAY

DISC

SUNFLOWER

SNAPDRAGON

PHLOX

BLUEBELL

FLOWERS WITH JOINED PARTS

classify the kinds of plants in a system which will reflect the actual course of their history—the unwritten history of their descent, through millions of years, from a smaller number of ancestors, from the first plants that ever lived. This is what is called the natural system of classification, as distinct from artificial systems such as that of Linnaeus. The English botanist John Ray had in fact proposed such a system (though he had no suspicion, apparently, of an evolution of different kinds), long before Darwin, even before Linnaeus; but the artificial system of Linnaeus was so neat, so usable, that it was adopted by almost every one, and Ray's never got the recognition which it merited.

Of course the past history of plants, and therefore their natural relationships, can only be inferred; probably we shall never be sure of them. We can only examine the present structure of plants, and note which parts seem least liable to change, which parts run through many diverse species. We are reasonably sure that the number of stamens, by itself, is not of much value as a guide; valerian and crocus, which are certainly unrelated, rub elbows in Linnaeus' system, while horse mint is separated from the other mints by most of the plant kingdom. As a guide to relationship we use groups of characters rather than single traits. Opinions have varied on what characters are most dependable. Charles Bessey, a great American teacher of botany, in the early years of this century announced a set of principles which have been more generally accepted than any others. Some of them are as follows:

1. Flowers with numerous parts, indefinite in number, came before those with fewer parts, definite in number (magnolia is more primitive than a lily).
2. Flowers with separate parts are more primitive than those with joined parts (a rose is more primitive, in this respect at least, than a primrose).
3. Regular flowers (lilies, roses) are primitive as compared with irregular flowers (sweet peas, snapdragons).
4. A long receptacle bearing floral members in a spiral (as in a magnolia) is considered primitive; a flat or hollow receptacle bearing the parts of the flower in circles or whorls (as in a rose or lily) is relatively advanced.

It is evident that a magnolia, on these principles, qualifies easily as the most primitive. A snapdragon, on the other hand, with its joined sepals, its joined and irregular petals, only five of each and only four stamens, the latter joined to the petals, and its compound pistil of two joined carpels, is relatively advanced. It is also worth noticing that a flower may be primitive in some respects and advanced in others. A wild rose, for example, has numerous stamens and carpels, an indefinite number of them, and all separate; its perianth is regular and composed of separate parts.

But the number of parts of the perianth is small and fairly definite; and the receptacle is of the advanced hollow type.

The extremes of the advanced tendencies enumerated above are found in that "royal family" of the flowering plants, the orchids. To attempt a detailed description of these flowers would be out of place here, since it necessitates a special vocabulary and a set of detailed diagrams. They are not only unusual in form, commonly beautiful in color, and often alluring in fragrance; they are intricate in structure and possess parts not found in other families. It must suffice here to indicate some of the general features of the family. There are three sepals and three petals. One of the petals is very different from the others, in many species enlarged and formed into a pouch or hollow "spur"; this is the "lip," often the most conspicuous part of the flower, as in a ladies'-slipper. In most orchids there is but one stamen, and this is joined with the style and stigma to form the "column" in the center. There are two masses of pollen connected by small stalks to an adhesive mechanism situated near the stigma (by which the pollen masses become attached to the back or to the proboscis of an insect; see below, p. 174). The ovary is inferior.

But the plant kingdom evolved in many different directions. The orchids may be considered a culminating point of evolution; but by no means the only one. In several other lines of descent the flowers did not become larger, more strikingly colored, more intricate; but just the opposite. Magnolia flowers are large; compare those of phlox and bluebell, bluets and rock cress and grapes —all relatively advanced types by Bessey's principles. Furthermore, not only does the number of parts become smaller and more definite; certain parts may be lost altogether. Many flowers have no petals, many have no perianth at all; look at the small flowers of cat-tail and pigweed, of willow and ash and oak, of the grasses and cereal grains.* In many kinds of plants there are two kinds of

---

* One of the older systems of classification was based on the supposition that these were the primitive types; that larger flowers with better-developed perianths came later. Modern studies have shown that in these apparently simple flowers there are remains of parts which have been lost; their simplicity is deceptive. However, the system was so widely used that it still forms the basis for the sequence of families in our manuals of botany.

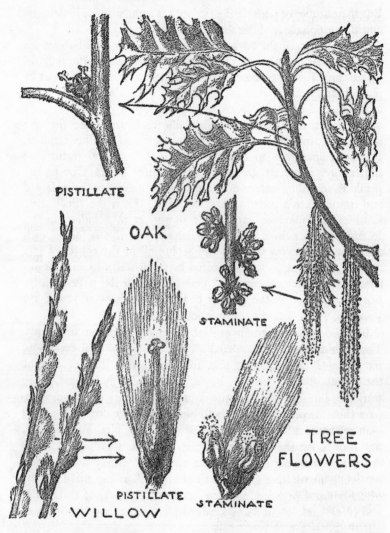

PISTILLATE

OAK

STAMINATE

PISTILLATE

WILLOW

STAMINATE

TREE FLOWERS

flowers, one having stamens but no pistils, the other pistils but no stamens; these kinds of flowers also usually lack petals, perhaps sepals also. Some willows bear flowers each consisting of nothing but a couple of stamens, standing beside the often downy scales that make the "pussies" of spring; other trees of the same species bear the pistillate flowers, each consisting of nothing but a pistil. An oak bears its staminate flowers on long dangling catkins; each flower is a cluster of stamens surrounded by a small green perianth. The pistillate flowers, which become the acorns, are on the same tree, in the axils of the leaves on the young branches; each flower consisting of a single compound pistil surrounded by a few scales (the future cup of the acorn). Hickories, alders, and many other trees and shrubs have similarly diminutive flowers, almost destitute of decorative qualities, reduced to the bare essentials, and with the two sexes separated. To the criteria already listed we may add:

5. Flowers with perianth are more primitive than those without (though here again notice that a flower may be primitive in one respect, advanced in others; the orchids have a perianth).

6. Plants with both stamens and pistils in the same flower are more primitive than those which have separate staminate and pistillate flowers.

As flowers became smaller, condensed as it were, there was also a tendency for them to become crowded in clusters. The large, primitive magnolia flower stands solitary at the end of its branch. The flowers of phlox, of snapdragon, of primrose, and many others are gathered in inflorescences of various types. The extreme of both condensation and aggregation of flowers is perhaps the common cat-tail of roadside ditches, lake borders, and swampy places generally. The cylindrical brown part, sometimes still seen in the "winter bouquet" that was more popular in the parlors of a generation ago, is made up of thousands of minute pistillate flowers, each consisting simply of a pistil and nothing more. Above them are the staminate flowers, similarly reduced to single stamens, and disappearing after the pollen has been shed.

It should be clear from the flowers just mentioned that small size and modesty of bearing do not lead to lack of success in the plant world. Indeed most of these families with inconspicuous flowers have been more successful—in terms of occupation of the earth—than the orchids and other exhibitionists. The grass family has evolved into thousands of species which cover vast steppes, savannas, and prairies; they include the cereals which are man's most important food and the pasture grasses which nourish his four-legged meat; the bamboos also, which are so important in the economy of southern Asia, are grasses. Yet their flowers are tiny, borne in loose panicles or close spikes. Each flower has a compound pistil of three carpels, which, however, contains but one ovule; surmounting the ovary are two long feathery styles. There are three stamens (six in bamboos), the pollen-bearing heads of which may dangle on long weak stalks. These make up the flower proper. There are a couple of minute scales at one side which some have considered to be the remains of a vanished perianth. All this is enclosed in a variety of scales, usually green, often hard and bristly, sometimes softly hairy; not strictly parts of the flower itself. These minute flowers are packed, singly or several together, into small scaly objects called "spikelets," many of which form the feathery or compact inflorescence. In maize, staminate flowers which lack pistils are crowded in the "tassel"; hundreds of pistillate flowers which have no stamens form the "ear"; the long styles with their feathery branches (which act as the stigma) are the "silk" which protrudes from the "husks."

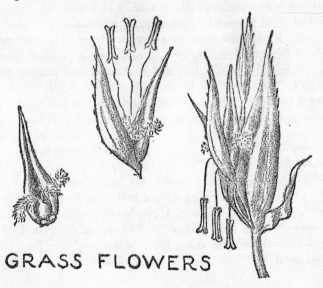

GRASS FLOWERS

The crowding of many small flowers in a tight cluster may lead us into error. There are, for instance, many sorts of dogwoods, all flowering plants; they have small flowers in large clusters, cymes. When we single out one sort as the "flowering dogwood" we are mistaking the four large white parts which beautify our plantings in spring for the petals of one flower; in reality they are leaves surrounding a close cluster of flowers; each of the small flowers has its own perianth, its own stamens and pistil, all complete.

In the poinsettias which form part of our Christmas celebration the flowers have almost disappeared. They are tiny, scarcely noticeable, each reduced to a single stamen or to a single pistil, with no perianth. The whole cluster of minute flowers is surrounded by the familiar colored leaves, which simulate petals. The calla lily likewise has a single large petal-like leaf around its cluster of little flowers; the latter are on the long spike which rises in the center of the "flower." Jack-in-the-pulpit and skunk cabbage belong to the same family; also the familiar philodendrons, some of which are grown as house-plants.

Some hydrangeas and viburnums have flowers of two types in the same cluster. The flowers around the margin form larger perianths and serve as a lure for insects; they are often sterile. The central flowers are less decorative but better provided with the essential reproductive parts. Of course man has been at pains to breed the central flowers out of existence and to produce a head of decorative but sterile flowers, as on the snowball bush; a state of affairs noticed by Andrew Marvell many years ago:

> "And in the cherry he does nature vex
> To procreate without a sex."

But of all the families which have arranged their several kinds of flowers in compact clusters, the most successful is the daisy family, that huge group which, besides daisies, includes thistles, ragweed, dandelion, goldenrod, and many other weeds of our fields and roadsides, the sage-brush and other shrubs of our deserts, many trees and shrubs of tropical America, and the lettuce, sunflowers, chrysanthemums, dahlias, zinnias, asters of our gardens.

The family is called the composite family from its inflorescence. The flower-heads resemble single flowers, so exactly are the individual flowers fitted together. The "flower" which the dahlia amateur proudly exhibits is really a head of many narrow flowers. In many species each head has two kinds of flowers: the sunflower has a disc surrounded by rays. Each disc flower has an erect narrow receptacle which contains the inferior ovary with its single ovule and is surmounted by the perianth and stamens. The sepals are merely a pair of scales.* The united petals form a narrow tube, dilated near the base into a sort of bulb, spreading at the tip into five teeth. The pollen-bearing parts of the stamens are joined, edge to edge, to form a sort of sleeve around the style. The flowers open in a regular sequence from the margin to the center of the disc.† As the petal-tips spread apart, the five stamens project. Then, after the pollen has been shed, these are withdrawn (pulled back by a coiling of their stalks into that basal bulb of the petal-tube) and the style rises from their midst, its two branches separating and exposing the stigmas. The ray flowers are similar, but have the petal-tube prolonged to one side to make the large yellow ray,‡ and they lack the reproductive parts. Some composites, such as the thistles, have only tubular flowers like the disc-flowers of the sunflower. Others have only flowers shaped like the ray flowers. Among the latter is the humble and despised dandelion; which may be said to share with orchids and crab-grass the distinction of being one of the culminating products of evolution in the plant world.

WHAT ARE FLOWERS FOR?

All the organization of a flower seems to be directed towards the transfer of pollen from stamen to pistil; a prelude to the formation of seed. In some kinds of plants the pollen is carried by the breezes and reaches a stigma by chance. In others the

---

* In many other members of the family, such as thistles and dandelions, the sepals are replaced by the familiar tuft of slender bristles.

† The head is one of the racemose group, in which the lowest or outermost flowers are often the first to open. See p. 146.

‡ In some varieties red or marked with red.

stamens may move so as to touch the stigma, in various remarkable ways. In most, however, the cooperation of animals is enlisted; a truly extraordinary partnership, in which the flowers are pollinated and the animals are fed. The animals in question are usually six-legged ones. Bees, beetles, butterflies, and other insects are thus caught up into the life of plants. Some kinds of flowers, however, are visited by birds or bats or even mice or snails; and these visitors also further the reproduction of plants.

The parts of flowers which cooperate in these events are so various, so intricate, so fraught with what seems to be meaning, that it is scarcely possible to describe them, to explain their mechanism, without reference to their "purposes." It is unfortunate that the purposes of things are not directly revealed to our observation. To write of these "contrivances" as if they had not been consciously designed, as if they were not directed towards a purpose, may rob one's description of any claim it may have to vivacity and truth, may leave it without color and perspective: a contribution by old Dryasdust himself. On the other hand, how can you know (unless he tells you) the purposes of your fellow creature? And as for plants, how are we to know even if they have purposes? Certainly we cannot include their intents among the data of science. To speak openly of the purposes of flowers which cooperate with insects is peculiarly silly, since one must in the same breath invoke the purposes of the insects also. The flower must have known that there is a certain kind of insect and must have set about making itself attractive and profitable to its intended dupe, besides devising a subtle mechanism which will ensure the transfer of pollen; and the insect must know about nectar and its connection with fragrance and color and it must provide itself with the right sort of proboscis to suck up the nectar; unwittingly it must also develop the bristles or other arrangements which will catch pollen—or all this bilateral scheming will be in vain. Such suppositions are beyond the capacity of a scientist, and indeed repugnant to common sense.

So, true to my scientific pretensions, I must abjure purposes and describe what happens, as nearly as I can, in purely objective terms. Yet it is difficult to believe (and I shall not insist) that all the truly astonishing adaptations of floral structure are the results of "pure chance," with some help from "natural selection."

The actual reproductive parts are the stamens and pistil. The first step in the production of seed is the transfer of pollen from stamen to stigma. Many flowers, as has been seen, have no other parts. This is particularly true of those that depend upon wind for pollination. Grasses, many trees (both coniferous and broad-leaved), the unlovely flowers of ragweed: such plants have little or no perianth. But the stigmas of such flowers are formed so as to comb out floating pollen from the air. The styles of a grass flower are disproportionally large when compared with the other parts, and much branched into delicate, hairlike filaments. All these hairs act as a stigmatic surface, and wherever in the feathery jungle a pollen grain alights it may germinate, start its fertilizing tube towards the ovule. Such is the silk of an ear of corn; the pollen tube must grow the vast distance from the tip of the ear down the delicate green-white filaments to the young grains within the husks. The stigmas of oak and willow and other trees are not so well developed as this; but they are broad in proportion to the size of the flower.

A second requisite for wind-pollinated plants is an abundance of pollen. If you shake a pine branch during the right season, a cloud of yellow dust like sulphur will fly out; pollen grains in incalculable numbers. Any sufferer from hay fever can testify to the prevalence of various pollens in the air. To be sure, only a small amount may be necessary to evoke the distressing symptoms in sensitive mucous membranes; but that small amount may have traveled many miles from the stamen which produced it. Only *a single pollen grain* is needed to ripen the seed within a grain of wheat or an acorn; but for that pollen grain to reach the stigma of that flower, pollen grains must have been cast on the air in incredible numbers, to float far and wide in all directions, and mostly to be wasted, to reach no stigma, to fertilize no seed.

Most kinds of flowers are familiar to us and valued by us mainly because of their perianths, particularly the petals which immediately surround the essential reproductive parts. The petals may be quite large, they are usually brightly colored in hues other than green, and frequently fragrant; all properties agreeable to insects, which can discern certain colors as well as we can, or better, and which apparently react positively to certain odors. The perianth may also form a convenient landing-place for six-legged visitors. Many kinds of flowers form nectar, which is essentially a dilute solution of sugar, food for small animals. In short, flowers provide free meals to those who can use them, and also publicize their wares.

The same is true even of flowers which we do not consider attractive—for some insects do not share our tastes. There are flowers that smell like carrion; and these are sought by flies, to which they presumably suggest a fit place for the deposition of eggs as well as a favorite food.

The nectar may be exuded by the petals or by certain bodies called nectaries which grow from the petals, from the stamens, from the pistil, or directly from the receptacle. It may collect in the bottom of the floral chalice, or in special petals or sepals which have parts shaped like sacs or horns or tubes, such as we see in larkspur, columbine, violets, orchids.

In any case things are so arranged that an insect probing towards the sweet liquid must come in contact with the pollen, which adheres to the opened heads of the stamens in rather sticky masses easily transferred to the hairy or bristly body or legs of the intruder. Some flowers do not leave this to chance; the insect is dusted with pollen by a more or less explosive discharge. This is well seen in mountain laurel. As the flower of this species opens, the tips of the stamens are caught in little pouches in the perianth, into which they grew in the bud; the spreading of the petals bends back the stamens, whose stalks are thus under considerable tension. A touch will release them from their strained position; they straighten up violently, throwing their loose pollen towards the center of the flower—towards the intruder responsible for their motion. A visiting insect is also likely to touch the stigma, whose sticky surface may filch some of the pollen from body or legs; perhaps a few grains only of the thousands formed, but sufficient for its "purposes."

It is clear that this transfer of pollen to pistil depends upon the

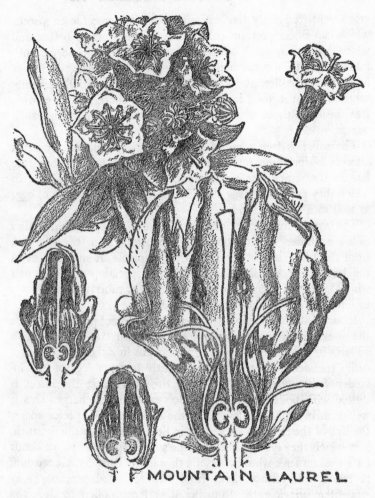

MOUNTAIN LAUREL

luring of insects to the flower and upon the placing of stamens and pistil in such positions that the insect must touch them in order to reach the nectar; and upon the production of large quantities of pollen of which most will not reach its "destination." The form of a flower must be understood in the light of these needs.

The pollen may be taken to the pistil of the same flower; to that of another flower of the same plant; to that of another flower of the same kind but on another plant; or even to that of a completely different kind of flower to which the wind may waft it or which the bee or butterfly or beetle may visit on its rounds. If pollen reaches the stigma of a different flower of the same plant, the *flowers* are cross-pollinated but the *plant* is self-pollinated. Plants are frequently cross-pollinated in nature as well as by plant growers.

Whether or not pollination is effective is another matter; it may or may not lead to the production of seed in the ovary of the pistil. To place pollen, say, of an apple blossom upon the stigma of a lily would not seem likely to yield results; the failure of cross-pollination does not surprise us. It is perhaps not so generally understood that self-pollination also may be ineffective. The results of pollination depend largely upon internal factors, in the pollen and in the pistil. The pollen of many petunias will remain inactive if placed on the stigma of its own flower, while if it is carried to a flower of another plant of the same kind it will initiate that series of events which results in the formation of seed. Such a plant is self-sterile, cross-fertile. Most varieties of blueberries have this peculiarity; radishes also; and many other kinds of plants. Many fruit trees go even farther: they are not only self-sterile, they fail to set seed even with pollen of other plants of the same variety; the *variety* is self-sterile. Though their behavior depends apparently on factors in the environment, and their sterility is therefore not absolute, many varieties of pears, including the popular Bartlett, are self-sterile, and other varieties are planted with them to ensure a crop. Most kinds of plants are sterile with pollen of other species; but many species of violets will "cross" freely with each other, yielding "hybrids"; and the crossability of orchids is one of their chief assets to the grower of these plants, who obtains new and valued forms by crossing species even in different genera.* At the

---

* As perhaps most gardeners know, the kinds of living things, plants and animals, are called species. The varieties which we recognize in the garden are subdivisions of species. All the red maples form one species; so do all the varieties of rose of Sharon. Closely related species form a genus (plural genera). All the maples, red and sugar and silver and Japanese, are one genus. The several species of one genus are more closely related than those of different genera; the various kinds of maples are more closely related than a maple is to an elm.

other extreme are many kinds of flowers—some cereals, for instance, and many violets—which regularly pollinate themselves.

This business of self- and cross-sterility is, as noticed above, not absolute: there are degrees of both. If a mixture of pollen is deposited on a stigma, it may be that all of it can start growth and any of it may be effective in seed production; but that pollen from another flower will grow more rapidly and so have more chance of contributing to the next generation than the pollen from the same flower. Or the opposite may be true.

THE WAY OF A FLOWER WITH A BEE

The older botanists, when they had realized the nature of stamens and pistils, spoke of flowers as mostly hermaphrodite, since they were obviously of both sexes; they assumed that they could fertilize themselves; and so they may. But the more abundant evidence which we have today shows that pollen is often ineffective on the stigma of the same flower. Moreover, many of the peculiarities of flowers are such as to ensure that the pollen does not stand much chance of even reaching the stigma of the same flower. In many flowers, for instance, the stigma is not exposed, can receive no pollen, at the time that the pollen of that flower is being shed from the stamens. In such flowers the stigma is displayed later; it is necessarily pollinated by some younger flower. This happens, for example, in delphinium, in various pinks, in geraniums, in the flowers of the carrot, and, as noticed above, in sunflowers. In other kinds of plants the reverse occurs: in strawberries and apple blossoms the stigma develops first and must receive pollen from some older flower, its own pollen being as yet unready. There is usually, however, some overlapping in the timing, so that self-pollination is just possible in the event that cross-pollination fails. This is particularly evident in such flowers as roses and hawthorns, which have many stamens; these open in sequence, the outer whorls first; by the time the inner stamens are shedding pollen, the stigmas of the flower are receptive.

Certain primroses have solved the problem in an entirely different way. Some species have two kinds of flowers. One kind has

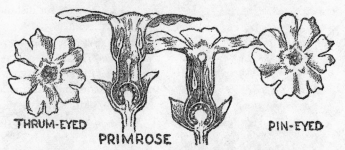

THRUM-EYED   PRIMROSE   PIN-EYED

stamens which project near the throat of the tubular joined petals (the stalks of the stamens are partly united to this tube); the stigma is carried on a short style and does not reach the same height as the stamens. When an insect of the appropriate size visits the flower, it enters the narrow tube head-downward, feeding on the nectar at the bottom; and later backs out. Pollen adheres to its hind-quarters, which were uppermost in the tube and in contact with the stamens. If this six-legged pollinator now enters another flower of the same kind, the pollen will not reach the stigma at the bottom of the tube. But in its travels it will probably find, on another plant of the same species, a flower with short stamens contained within the tube and a long style which carries the stigma up to the throat of the tube. It is easy to see what happens: the pollen from the first flower, carried on the insect's hind-parts, is now caught by the stigma of the second kind of flower. And meanwhile the insect picks up new pollen on its foreparts, which can only be caught by a stigma in a flower of the first kind. The two kinds of flowers are called "thrum-eyed" and "pin-eyed" according as the stamens or the stigma is visible in the throat. There are also two kinds of pollen, the larger grains being compatible with the longer styles, the smaller with the shorter.

There are even flowers which arrange their reproductive parts at *three* levels; the purple loosestrife is an example.

But if such a precise disposition of parts in a flower provokes our wonder, what are we to think of a violet? This pretty flower, symbol of humility, is a complex mechanism which ensures cross-pollination and prevents self-pollination. It stands horizontally and one petal, the lowest, is larger than the others, forming a

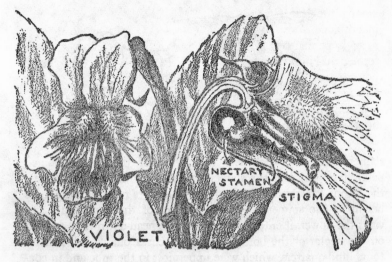

VIOLET

NECTARY
STAMEN

STIGMA

landing-stage for insects. A small club-shaped style, with the stigma
in a hollow on the lower side, projects in the center; the five
stamens invest the style very closely, being in contact edge to
edge; but the knob-like end of the style emerges from the sleeve
which they form. From the two lower stamens depend two large
nectaries; the sweet stuff which they exude drips down into the
lowest petal, which has a hollow extension behind, the "spur."
The stamens open along their *inner* surfaces, so that the pollen
is held in the sheath which they form around the style; it cannot
possibly reach the stigma outside this sheath. But when an insect
alights on the lowest petal and pushes in towards the confection
which awaits it within, in the spur, it must touch the hanging
nectaries; this causes a movement of the stamens, and some pollen
falls from the chinks between them onto the visitor. As it backs
out, it may rub off some pollen, but *not on the stigma*; for this is
in a depression which faces outward. It is easy, however, for some
of the pollen to be rubbed off onto the stigma of another flower,
as the insect enters it.

Actually this elaborate scheme seems to be too good! These
flowers often fail to set much seed. But wait—there is more to
come. Another sort of flower is formed by the same plant, usually
a little later. Its stem is short and the flower usually lies unnoticed

among the leaf-stalks; it may be practically underground. It is inconspicuous also for another reason: it never opens. Its sepals form a permanent bud (permanent, that is, until the fruit is formed and pushes them apart); within this the rudimentary petals fail to grow. Stamens and pistil, however, are fully developed; and in this flower the stamens surround the entire pistil, *stigma and all*. The pollen is but a short distance from the stigma, with no obstacle intervening; and though it never reaches the stigma as a pollen grain, it sprouts a small tube which covers the space between and brings about fertilization.

The first kind of flower, the familiar blue or lavender or white or yellow flower which every one knows, can set seed only when provided by a visitor of the appropriate kind with pollen from another flower. The second kind can only be pollinated by itself. If insects fail the plant, seed will be formed anyhow. So violets carry on their manifold species and varieties: numerous crosses are found in nature; and large numbers of plants are formed by self-pollination.

The apparently conscious cooperation between insect and flower is sometimes hard to believe. A flower of yucca can be pollinated only by a certain kind of moth. This insect first lays eggs in the ovary, then actually gathers pollen and carries it to the stigma, pressing it down there with all the care of a plant breeder intent on the production of a new hybrid. The pollen fertilizes the many ovules, which develop into many seeds. The eggs of the moth grow into small worms which feed on the seeds. But there are more seeds than worms and some remain to propagate the yucca. Pollination without egg-laying would be of no use to the moth; nor would egg-laying without pollination, for the worms would then have nothing to eat. Pollination without eggs would presumably suit the plant; but it can afford to sacrifice some of its hundreds of potential seeds for a certain and safe method of pollination.

But of all the wonderful, the incredible mechanisms which press small animals into the service of plants, nothing excels those of the orchids. These various "devices" are of a bewildering variety and complexity. It must suffice here to describe a single example; and that of the simplest.

The general structure of the flower of an orchid has been already briefly outlined. The essential parts are united to form the central column. On the front of this the broad sticky stigma may be seen. At the summit is the upper part, the pollen-bearing head, of the single stamen. Just above the stigma and below the pollen chamber is a sort of flap, the rostellum. In a cattleya the under side of the rostellum is covered with a viscid matter. There are two masses of pollen, connected by small strings which pass below the rostellum. The whole column is almost enveloped in the beautifully colored lip, the most conspicuous part of the flower; this serves not only for the adornment of ladies but as a tunnel through which an insect in search of sweetness must pass and which leads it inevitably to the rostellum near the tip of the protruding column. As soon as the visitor touches this and forces it back, a quantity of the viscid matter is squeezed out and sets instantly like cement on the intruding proboscis or head; in this are entangled some of the threads attached to the pollen grains. When the insect is satisfied and withdraws, it will drag one or both of the pollen masses from their chamber, and during the rest of its travels will wear them as dangling but firmly fastened adornments. Of course as flower after flower is visited, of the same or closely related kinds, the pollen will be carried up inside the lip and pushed against the broad stigma; and some grains from the pollen masses will be caught on the sticky surface.

In other orchids the pollen masses are attached to small tails or stems which become cemented to the insect and which stand erect upon its head or back, bearing the pollen-masses like plumes. They may even be ejected like projectiles when the visitor touches certain sensitive antennae; flying with their sticky discs forward like toy arrows fitted with suction-cups. A further refinement (described eloquently by Charles Darwin many years ago) is a contraction of the cement, after it has set, in such a manner that the pollen-bearing stalks are bent down and point forward; when the insect enters another flower, the pollen-masses will not be pushed back into an empty pollen-chamber like the one from which they were taken, but against the stigma just below this. In the marvelous display of an orchid, no detail seems to have been forgotten to make winged guests efficient pollinators.

8

❦❦❦❦❦

Seed and Fruit

AFTER POLLINATION, WHAT?

How does the transfer of some yellow or white or pink or blue dust to the stigma, however ingeniously effected, help in the formation of seed in the ovary? That the pollen does indeed play a part in this process was known to Egyptians and Assyrians thousands of years ago; they used to hang branches of staminate flowers of the date-palms among the clusters of pistillate flowers, to make sure of fruit. More recently and more generally, it was known to Linnaeus and his contemporaries. But ideas on just what happens were mixed. Some thought that the pollen burst and freed something which traveled through the style and reached the ovules; some impalpable fluid or minute particles. Then in the nineteenth century, as microscopes and the techniques of using them improved, it was found that the pollen grain *grows* when it lands on the proper stigma; it sends forth a long, slender, transparent thread containing living matter. It will often do this in a dish containing a dilute solution of sugar; its germination may be observed through the microscope; it is more difficult but still possible to detect its growth through the style and into the ovary. For in nature that is what the thread, the pollen tube, does: it grows down the style, either boring its way through or following the interior cavity if there is one, until it reaches the ovary.

A remarkable event, this germination and growth of the pollen. There may be hundreds of grains deposited on a stigma; hundreds of tubes growing within the style. The grains, as they start their growth, absorb something from the stigma, water and food,

175

perhaps vitamins and other things; the tubes emerge through thin places in the hard walls of the grains, grow into the style like so many threads of parasitic fungi, feeding on the pistil as they grow, on their own parent perhaps. They enter the ovary, perhaps in their hundreds; and each directs its course unerringly towards an ovule. Why? This is a question for future researchers. We know *what they do*, but not *what causes them to do it*.

When it arrives in the ovary, the pollen tube penetrates an ovule. What then? In the time of Linnaeus' greatness, the second half of the eighteenth century, Sir John Hill argued that he could see the new plant, the embryo, in the pollen grain; this embryo, he believed, migrated down the pollen tube into the ovule, where it grew to the proper size. An eminent German botanist of little more than a hundred years ago, Matthias Schleiden, thought that the end of the tube becomes the embryo in the seed, as the ovule ripens and enlarges, the ovule furnishing only nutriment; and he drew pictures which proved it—at least to his satisfaction. But finally, with the development of more modern microscopes and more modern methods of preparing pistils and pollen grains for microscopic examination, the truth was discovered. Something—but not the embryo—does pass down through the pollen tube into the ovule and enter into the formation of the new generation; there is also something in the ovule—not merely nutriment—which helps to form the embryo. Both pollen and ovule contribute to the formation of the new plant; each of them contributes a *single living cell*.

The very young ovule is an oval solid body, attached by a short stalk to the side of the ovary, or perhaps to one of its partitions if the pistil is compound, or to a column which rises from its floor; it often bends on its stalk so that its tip is near the point of attachment. As it develops, a fold arises near its base and all around its girth and grows forward towards its apex; forming a sort of cup or sheath around it like the cup around the lower part of an acorn. There may be a second fold outside the first. These folds, which form a sort of outer skin to the ovule (open at the apex), are called integuments.

The central part of the ovule contains a minute, very watery or juicy body which has received the curious name of embryo-sac.

It consists of several cells, separated only by very delicate membranes, scarcely to be seen in the living state.

The pollen grain when it is first formed is a single cell; but this cell divides, and (usually) by the time it is shed from its stamen and carried to a stigma, it consists of two cells. One of these consists of little but a nucleus and floats within the cytoplasm of the other—a cell within a cell. The large cell, which still occupies most of the space within the grain, becomes that pollen tube which has already been mentioned. As it grows into a tube, it becomes more and more watery; its nucleus is usually to be found near the actively growing tip. The other cell, still contained within the tube cell, again divides, forming two slim cells which float or swim down the tube. Sometimes they seem to be carried passively in the streaming cytoplasm of the tube; sometimes they are seen to move, to undulate like minute worms.

The tip of the pollen-tube characteristically grows into the apex of an ovule, through the opening left by the integuments

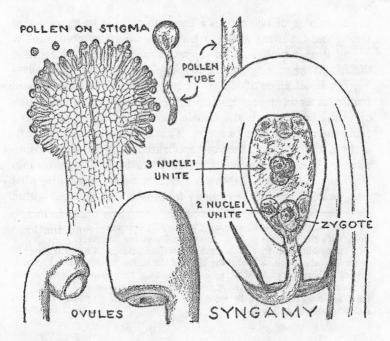

POLLEN ON STIGMA

POLLEN TUBE

3 NUCLEI UNITE

2 NUCLEI UNITE

ZYGOTE

OVULES

SYNGAMY

(though it may sometimes bore right into the ovule from its base). It penetrates the central part of the ovule and enters the embryo-sac; and there bursts, discharging its contents. One of the swimming cells above-mentioned then *unites* with one of the cells of the embryo-sac. The cytoplasm of the two becomes merged, so that both nuclei lie in a common unit of living matter; then the nuclei themselves approach one another, come into contact, lose the boundary which separates them, and become one nucleus. The opposite of cell division has occurred: from two cells one has been formed. *This single cell* is the begining of the embryo, the new generation.

The union of two cells is called, technically, syngamy. More loosely it is spoken of as fertilization. The only difficulty with the latter term is that it has been used also for the transfer of pollen from stamen to stigma, the fertilizing act that must precede the actual union of cells; this is generally called pollination. (Fertilization may also refer, of course, to the fertility of soil, in the nutritive sense.)

This joining of two cells is a common prelude to reproduction throughout the living world; or perhaps it would be more accurate to call it an essential act of reproduction. The cells which have the faculty of uniting are called gametes.* They are generally— but not in all kinds of plants—of two kinds; call them male and female, or by whatever technical names you prefer.† In most kinds of plants and animals the female gamete, or egg, is the larger; while the male gamete, or sperm, is smaller and has the power of motion. Furthermore, they are specialized in other, less obvious ways. Neither (with some exceptions) can by itself develop into anything; the union of the two seems to supply something that each lacks, to release the capacity for growth that is latent within

---

* From the Greek word meaning "married." "Syngamy" is from the same word, with the addition of "syn" from the Greek for "together."

† Those who wish to draw a close comparison between the sexual processes of plants and animals call them the egg and the sperm, or egg cell and spermatozoid. Others, more wary of such comparisons, have named them merely by their comparative size: megagamete and microgamete. All terms (and there are more) are open to some objections. For our purposes "male and female gametes" will suffice.

them. The cell which results from this union, called the zygote,* has this capacity for growth; sometimes after a period of dormancy, but often at once, it begins its development. It divides into two cells, then into four, and so on; the new cells enlarge, they assume the character proper to their species and to their position in the organism; a new individual is on the scene.

In the flowering plants with which we are here concerned, the zygote develops at once into the embryo; that plantlet which, long ago, you watched emerging from its coverings and forming its roots, its stem, its leaves, finally to take its place among the adornments of your garden. The embryo does not flow down the pistil from the pollen grain; it does not grow from a transformation of the end of the pollen tube. It is formed within the ovule, within the embryo-sac, formed from a single cell, a zygote; which itself was formed by the union of two gametes. The old botanists were not so far wrong when they thought that some minute grains or some impalpable fluid traveled down the style into the ovary; it is a living cell, the male gamete, which makes that journey. The female gamete which is needed to complete the process awaits it within the ovule.

As the gametes unite in the embryo-sac, as the zygote begins its development into an embryo, another and equally remarkable event occurs, in the same embryo-sac. There were *two* male gametes in the pollen-tube; only *one* unites with the female gamete in the embryo-sac. But the other one is not wasted. It moves to the center of the embryo-sac and its nucleus there encounters two other nuclei, one of which has come from each end, each pole of the sac: the so-called polar nuclei. *All three* of these nuclei unite, forming one oversized nucleus. This divides into two, the daughter nuclei divide into four, and so on; cell walls may ultimately be formed; and the endosperm has begun its career. This is that mass of cells which lays in a supply of food and which, at least for a time, partly or wholly envelops the embryo. Its subsequent history is very various. It may be imperfectly formed into cells and remain partly or wholly a liquid, a rich and nutritious liquid; as in a coconut. It may form a rock-like mass of thick-walled cells,

* From the Greek word for "yoked."

as in a date seed. Or it may, as we have already seen, be at once consumed by the growing embryo, which takes over its function of food-accumulation.

Embryo and endosperm are partners, having a somewhat similar and almost simultaneous origin; both growing and filling up the embryo-sac; finally becoming much larger, greatly exceeding in volume the original ovule in which they were formed. But the ovule has also grown larger. Stimulated in some way by these events within it, it has enlarged greatly, has formed various sorts of special outer layers; it has become, in short, the seed-coat which surrounds embryo and endosperm (or embryo alone if the endosperm has been devoured by the embryo).

This is the origin of that complex body, the seed. Whether it is a mustard seed or a coconut, a bean or an almond or the stone of a date, it was formed from the outer layers of an ovule, from the union of two gametes, and from the joining of three other cells in the ovule.*

FRUITS FOR THE TABLE

After flowering comes fruit. All the extraordinary doings of flowers with other living creatures, all the complex functioning of the pollen and the embryo-sac, the generation of a new plant or of many new plants—all these come to visible fruition in the diverse productions that we pluck from trees or gather from vines, that we harvest and reap and thresh, and subsequently freeze and can and preserve in hundreds of ways. All fruits are from flowers.

The young plant, the embryo, is well guarded against the

---

* One of the things that makes the teaching of biology difficult is that general statements are often untrue; the above is one of these. In some kinds of plants more or less than three nuclei participate in the formation of endosperm. There are also plants in which the female cell, the egg in the embryo-sac, can develop into an embryo without the aid of any male cell. In some plants other cells in the ovule have this power also; this comes close to being a form of vegetative reproduction, the formation of a new individual from cells not usually directly involved in that process.

The outlines of the story given above are true for many species and may be considered the normal course of events.

vicissitudes of the outer world. It is enclosed in a seed-coat; and often in an endosperm lying between it and the seed-coat. But— as we may have forgotten in threading our way through this long history—the ovule itself is sheltered; it lies within the ovary at the base of the pistil in or near the center of the flower.

The pistil is usually minute, its ovary perhaps as big as the head of a pin; the ovules are often hard to see without a magnifier. But as the enlarging ovules become seeds they do not burst out from the surrounding walls of the ovary; for this becomes more capacious. As the seeds grow the ovary also grows; and it changes its texture, becoming perhaps hard and woody, perhaps soft and juicy; usually it changes to a color different from its original hue; its final state bears little resemblance to its first. A few examples may lend cogency to these statements.

A tomato was once the ovary of a pistil, a minute green thing. When it is fully grown and ripe it has a volume perhaps 100,000 times what it was at flowering time; it is red instead of green; and

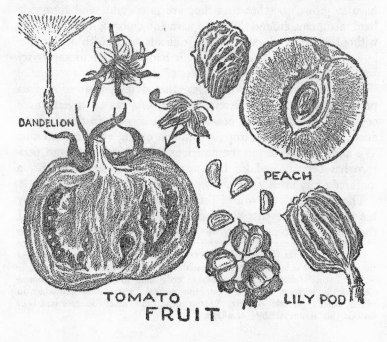

DANDELION

PEACH

TOMATO
FRUIT

LILY POD

more than nine-tenths water. It has changed also chemically, with the formation of sundry acids and esters and vitamins and sugars. A grape also is a matured ovary (with or without seeds). A peach, a plum, a cherry—these are ovaries; skin, flesh, and stone all develop from the base of the pistil (the one or two seeds, of course, are within the stone). Moreover, these three had much the same appearance in the beginning; during their development they acquired their well-known differences in size, color, and taste. A date has the same beginning; but in it the stone itself is the seed. A pea-pod derives from the same part of a flower; so do the bean-pods which we eat in the young state as "string beans." The shell of an acorn develops from an ovary; also the shell of a coconut. A grain of buckwheat is not a seed, though it looks like one; it is a fully developed ovary, with a single seed within. Strangely enough a grain of corn or wheat or oats is the same: it is not a seed, but a matured ovary containing a seed. In the grass family, to which these cereal grains belong, seed-coat and surrounding ovary have so grown together that they are inseparable and form one hard membrane around the endosperm and embryo; it is impossible without microscopic study (and difficult even with it) to say how much of the skin of the grain had its origin in the ovary wall, how much in the outer layers of the ovule.

From this brief survey it is clear that development of a given part may take many different courses. Objects so diverse as a coconut, a tomato, and a pea-pod do not suggest, in their appearance, in their size or texture, a common origin; yet they had one. We need a name for all these various productions; the word pericarp has been coined for the purpose.* A pericarp is simply a matured ovary usually containing one or more seeds.†

The remarkable growth of the ovary seems to be stimulated by the reproductive events which occur in the pistil. The arrival of the pollen has something to do with it. Grapes will not develop

---

* Peri-, around, as in "perianth"; karpos, "fruit"; signifying the fruit around the seed(s); but defined botanically much more precisely as above.

† In nature fruits regularly contain seeds; but in cultivation we grow many fruits without seeds, without the normal processes of reproduction which usually precede fruiting. So our definitions must be broadened to include this abnormal state of affairs.

unless pollination occurs. The pollen may not form gametes; or the gametes may not reach the embryo-sac; no embryo may be formed, and no seed; yet the pericarp develops. Something must come from the pollen grain and flow down through the stigma and style into the ovary, something besides the pollen tube; this is not mere speculation, like the ideas of Linnaeus, for we know that substances do move through plants which have a decisive influence on their development—the growth substances. A number of experimenters have recently been busy spraying auxin and other substances on the stigmas of just-opened flowers (at the same time preventing pollen from reaching them). The results have been striking. Seedless fruits can be thus produced, at will, in some kinds of plants. Some progress has been made towards doing this on a commercial scale.

In other plants the development of the pericarp seems to depend on syngamy and on the development of the embryo, rather than on pollination alone. In the pistils of many apple flowers something goes wrong with the processes of reproduction. The embryo begins its development, but fails; the fruit likewise starts to enlarge, but soon ceases and falls to the ground—often in June in the northeastern United States: the "June drop" is only too familiar to orchardists.

Enough has been said of the diversity of pericarps to show that a common origin does not mean final resemblance. The products of the development of ovaries of different species of plants differ as much as the trunk of an oak differs from the stem of a tomato plant, or the leaf of a pitcher-plant from that of a cactus. It is equally true that the resemblance of two objects does not always mean that they had the same origin. The succulent fruits mentioned above—tomatoes, grapes, peaches—are all pericarps; all developed from ovaries. But melons and bananas and apples and pears and quinces and blueberries are more complex; they are derived from other parts of flowers *in addition to* the ovaries. And a strawberry or a raspberry or a pineapple or a fig involves several distinct ovaries or even several distinct flowers that are closely associated together.

To understand such matters it is necessary to turn back to the flowers which are their first manifestations; for all fruits come from flowers. In an apple blossom, for instance, the sides of the ovary (composed typically of five carpels joined in the center) are fused with the cup-shaped receptacle in which it stands. This entire body becomes the apple—ovary and receptacle.*

A melon has a similar derivation: at least the tough rind is formed from parts of the flower outside of the inferior ovary but adhering to it. The same is true of bananas and blueberries and gooseberries and currants. And even some of the things usually called seeds are not only more than seeds, they are more than pericarps. Sunflower "seeds," which you perhaps grow for the oil which may be expressed from them, or buy for the chickadees in your garden, take their origin in the lower parts of those composite flowers described above (p. 164). Each is derived from the receptacle with its contained and inseparable ovary and each contains one seed; the apparent "seed" is a fruit. The same is true of a dandelion "seed," that pest of our lawns; the long beak on its summit is the upper part of the receptacle; the crown of white hairs represents the sepals; of the original flower only the petals and stamens are missing.

Strawberries and raspberries and blackberries come from flowers which have many simple pistils—single carpels like those of a magnolia or buttercup or rose; they grow on a sort of knob in the center of the flower, a part of the receptacle. A raspberry is formed of all the pericarps which grow from these pistils; as they enlarge they touch one another and lightly cohere. Each individual pericarp is like a small cherry: skin and juicy flesh and stone, and a seed within the stone. All the pericarps come off together, when they are ripe, forming the familiar thimble-shaped berry. In a blackberry the knob-like part of the receptacle comes off too, forming a part of the fruit, and serving to hold all the pericarps more firmly together. A strawberry is actually the receptacular knob, much enlarged and transformed into something red, succulent, and delicious. The pericarps are still on its surface; they are what we usually call the seeds, but each is a minute nut containing a seed.

---

* And the joined basal parts of perianth and stamens too, according to some botanists; see the note on p. 153.

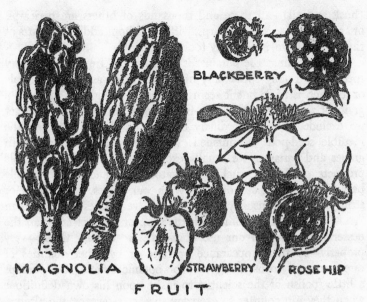

BLACKBERRY

MAGNOLIA STRAWBERRY ROSE HIP
FRUIT

A pineapple is really a mass of flowers, an inflorescence, in which most parts have become succulent. The petals and stamens fall; but the sepals and ovaries (in the cultivated varieties without seeds) are all crowded together into one edible fruit. A fig is comparable; but it has its flowers *inside* the enlarged end of the stem; again what we call the "seeds" are really small nutlike pericarps, which have developed from the ovaries of the numerous flowers within, and each of which may contain a seed. What we eat is the stem on which all these minute flowers grew.

And so with all the delicious fruits which adorn our tables, and many other things which we do not eat but which are botanically similar. Apples and pears and cherries and bananas and oranges and figs and strawberries and mulberries, and the pods of peas and beans and lilies and larkspurs and okra, and the bolls of cotton and the burs of cocklebur and burdock, and the grains of corn and barley and rice and blue-grass and buckwheat, and sun-flower "seed" and beggarticks and sticktights, and the keys of maple and of ash, and acorns and peanuts in the shell and coconuts (husk and all)—all these and thousands of others are pericarps, or are made of several pericarps, with or without additional parts of the flowers from which they took their being.

All these things the botanist is apt to term "fruit." In ordinary speech we usually speak only of edible things as fruit; an apple or a peach is fruit, but it seems strange to include an acorn or a grain of wheat or a cocklebur in the same category. And in fact we exclude from our ordinary concept of "fruit" not only the inedible seed-pods or nutshells which have a like origin with grapes and bananas; we usually exclude also some of the edible products of flowers, such as tomatoes and cucumbers, merely because we use them differently on our tables. Okra pods or string beans we usually think of as "vegetables" rather than "fruit," because they come with the soup or meat rather than the dessert. In short, in our use of words, we classify things—very properly—by their appearance or taste or by other qualities of direct concern to us rather than by botanical facts. It is perhaps a little foolish of the scientist to insist upon his own definitions when they run counter to everyday speech. However, the alternative would be for him to adopt an entire new vocabulary for these familiar things, these seeds and fruits; and we should have to learn it also if we wanted to understand the botanist. So we must humor him to some extent. In the botanical sense, a seed is always formed from an ovule, and from nothing exterior to this. The part which immediately encloses the ovule, in the flowering plants, is the ovary; and this, when it matures, is the pericarp.* Fruit, to the botanist, means that which encloses the seed (or which would enclose the seed if there were any). It always involves at least a pericarp; and may be formed from many pericarps, coming from one or many flowers, and from other parts of the flower or flowers also. Whether it is edible, or useful to man in any way, is beside the point.

Are fruits of any use to plants? This question is easily answered for sticktights and beggarticks. They are adhesive, they cling to passing animals, and so acquire the temporary use of four legs—or

---

* The conifers also form seeds from ovules; but their ovules are not in ovaries, and no pericarps develop. See p. 208.

at least of two. This favors their chances of finding a good place in which to germinate; for it is obviously to their advantage to get away from the shadow of their parents; apron strings may have too repressive an influence.

Everyone, I suppose, has watched the keys of maple drift down from the tree, whirling as they slowly fall and caught by any chance breeze. It is almost needless to mention the dandelion, which succeeds only too well in getting about. Some fruits actually eject their seeds, with considerable force, and to some distance. There is a sort of explosive wild cucumber which squirts them out; and the pods of touch-me-not break and curl up at a slight contact, scattering the seeds and furnishing a reason for the name. Likewise the succulent fruits aid in the dispersion of their species over the earth. If they are eaten by birds—and if you have ever watched the disappearance of a crop of cherries from your garden you know that they *are* eaten by birds—the stones or hard seeds within them may be carried through the air for miles within the digestive tracts of their feathered consumers, and may finally be deposited unharmed in some distant spot as yet uncolonized by that species; they acquire wings instead of legs. The succulent fruits have another use. Even if they fall straight to earth, as an apple or persimmon does, the abundant and nutritious tissue which makes up the fruit and surrounds the seeds quickly decays and replenishes the soil, providing a fertile spot for the growth of the seedlings.

We are, in short, here again confronted with a wealth of "devices" which ensure the success of plants in their strange lives. It is as well to be cautious, and to eschew careless talk of the "purposes" of fruits. The cocklebur is obviously made to be transported by animals—if anything is obvious. But the animals carry the burs to distant hilltops and meadows, which the plants are not very successful in colonizing; and new tangles of cockleburs spring up most abundantly in the creek bottoms, where the fruits are carried by the rains of autumn. If you must talk of the purposes of plants and their parts, it would be just as safe to say that the purpose of a bean is to be eaten; for that is what happens to most of them.

But, speaking objectively, it is true that in the main fruits help flowering plants to spread abroad and to become established in new places.

SLEEP

When a seed reaches maturity—it goes to sleep. The embryo, having formed its several parts, suspends growth. The endosperm around it, if there is any, rests with its quota of food. The seed-coat around all is a protective shell (or the inner layer of the pericarp may form such a protective covering, the seed-coat itself being thin; as in an almond or walnut).

Of course plants do not really sleep, in the sense that we do. They can scarcely lose consciousness, not having any to lose. But they do suspend activity in a somewhat analogous manner. The botanists say that they become dormant—which is another way of saying that they go to sleep. Other parts of plants also become dormant. The buds of trees and shrubs and vines do so, at least in climates that endure alternating periods of drought and moisture or heat and cold. The buds on our oaks and elms and maples become dormant late in the summer; they resume growth—germinate—the following spring. Buds may lie dormant many years and still germinate.

A dormant bud or seed is not completely inactive, any more than a sleeping animal is. Complete cessation of all the processes of a living thing is death; and once death has arrived, life does not return. Tests of sufficient delicacy have shown that there is a tiny flow of energy through the cells of dormant seeds and buds—energy derived from respiration, from the breakdown of food. But growth has ceased; there is no formation of new parts; essentially nothing is happening. Life continues—but only barely.

Seeds may sleep for many years, and still germinate. Tales of living peas taken from the tomb of Tutankhamen, and of viable wheat grains from other Egyptian tombs thousands of years old, are only examples of man's regrettable propensity for preying on innocent tourists; they are fabrications. But quite recently it has been shown that living lotus seeds found in a peat bog in China, at first thought to have lain there a mere 250 years or so, are actually more than 1,000 years old.

Most seeds do not live nearly so long. In 1879 William James Beal of Michigan Agricultural College started a famous experiment. He put seeds of 22 kinds of plants—mostly common weeds—in each of 20 pint bottles, and buried them 18 inches deep in the ground. At intervals thereafter a bottle was dug up and the seeds in it tested for their power to germinate. After 25 years 11 of the original 22 species had viable seeds; after 40 years 8; and after 70 years only 3. Seeds of many garden plants are not good for more than 10 years, some not for more than two. Seeds of soft maple, beech, various oaks, walnuts and hickories, sugar cane, the rubber tree—these must germinate in a short time, a matter of months, or they will forever lose the power to do so. It has been found, however, that the life of such short-lived seeds may be considerably prolonged by storing them under certain conditions—the conditions differing with the species. The life of many garden seeds may be lengthened by keeping them away from contact with air and moisture and at a low temperature.

Some of the long-lived seeds are hard to awaken. Seeds of legumes—lupines and the like—are notorious for this. Their prolonged dormancy is due to the hardness of their seed-coats, which prevents the passage of water into the embryo. Some seeds of the geranium family, the morning-glory and potato families, and others, have the same peculiarity; and the lotus seeds already mentioned. In nature such seeds must lie dormant many years, even hundreds or thousands of years, before their seed-coats are sufficiently decomposed to allow germination. In our gardening, since we cannot wait indefinitely, the seeds are subjected to various treatments to break their dormancy: the seed is nicked with a file or soaked in sulphuric acid.

In other kinds of seeds the embryo is incapable of growth until certain inner processes, certain chemical changes, have been completed: this is called "after-ripening." This is what we find in the seeds of roses and apples and some maples. The ripening may be hastened by storing the seed at a low temperature; in this way we may germinate a rose seed after six months instead of having to wait five years.

Still other refractory seeds have impervious coats *and* unripe embryos; seeds of basswood, of the bunchberry (herbaceous dogwood), of cotoneaster are of this type. They must be treated with *both* sulphuric acid and low temperature.

The advantages to the plant of a period of dormancy are fairly obvious. The seed is formed in an ovary, a part of a flower, perhaps high on tree or shrub, at least at some distance from the ground even on an herbaceous plant.* If the embryo could not stop its growth, the seed would have to be dropped to earth at precisely the right moment for the emergence of the root. Some plants, it is true, behave almost in this way: the trees already mentioned with short-lived seeds, for example. But most seeds have their dormant period to carry them through the process of dissemination; they take their time. They can be forcibly ejected from their pods, wafted by winds to great distances, even passed through the alimentary tracts of birds and beasts; sooner or later to find a patch of moist earth and put forth root and stem and leaves and begin to shift for themselves with a fair chance of success in the battle of life.

Most weed seeds, as we know to our cost, are long-lived. Once the lawn is infested with crab-grass, new plants continue to appear for many years, even if we are successful in avoiding fresh contamination. Individual seeds of the same kind germinate after different periods of rest, so that after an initial seeding one species will continue to make its appearance through a long succession of years. So the habit of sleeping late can contribute to the success of a species.

HEREDITARY COMPLICATIONS

Heredity has puzzled the curious and exercised the ingenious for many centuries. What makes a seed grow in the likeness of the plant it came from? Why do seeds from some plants

* Except for the peanut vine, which actually plants its legumes in the earth by means of elongation of their stalks.

grow uniformly, all much alike, while those from other parents become plants of various sizes, shapes, and colors? How does it happen that sometimes a plant does not resemble its immediate parent or parents but some more remote ancestor? Why, when you cross two inbred lines of maize, are you likely to get plants all alike in appearance and equally vigorous; while if you grow another generation from these in turn you get an assortment of strong and weak plants of varied characteristics? (And of course all these questions are asked about the reproduction of animals also.)

Some of these questions have been answered, at least partly, in an earlier chapter (pages 133-136). The development of certain colors, of certain forms, of certain sizes is governed by things called genes which are situated in threads called chromosomes in the nuclei of cells. When new cells are formed the chromosomes are accurately halved and complete samples of each are distributed to every daughter cell; so that these have the same possibilities for development as the parent cell had. When you grow a new potato plant from a meristematic bit of an old plant, the cells in that meristem all have the same set of chromosomes as those in the old plant. Given the same surroundings in which to grow, they will produce a plant with characteristics like those of the parent. The same is true of all the different kinds of vegetative reproduction described on previous pages. That intricate process called mitosis is responsible for hereditary resemblance. But what about seeds? Are they also formed by mitosis? And if so, what about the questions raised above, and many other problems of heredity?

The plant which you grow from seed was once an embryo. The embryo grew from one cell, the zygote. Whatever inherent, inherited material the new plant has, whatever can be traced to its parentage, was once contained in that single cell. But it, in turn, was derived from two cells, two gametes: one from the pollen, the other from the embryo-sac. The inheritance of the new generation is traceable to those two cells, which came from the parent plant or plants.

What happens to the chromosomes, to the genes, when cells *unite*? Each of the gametes, the male gamete from the pollen and the female gamete from the embryo-sac, has a nucleus; in each nucleus is a complete set of chromosomes, like that of any other cell of that species. When they are joined, when their two nuclei become one nucleus, their chromosomes *do not unite*. The zygote has *two complete sets* in its single nucleus. As it divides into two and the daughter cells again divide, as these cells grow into a mature plant, each chromosome is split in the usual way and the halves distributed to the daughter cells. Every cell of the plant has two sets of chromosomes. We express this state of affairs by referring to the zygote and to the plant which grows from it as diploid. Cells which have but a single set of chromosomes, such as the gametes, are called haploid.*

But what happens when this diploid plant itself forms gametes and they unite to form a new zygote? Will the new gametes be diploid like their parent and will the zygote now have *four* sets of chromosomes? Although such things do sometimes happen, it needs no great imagination to see that if this were the normal course of events in reproduction, conditions in the plant kingdom would soon be chaotic.

Such a disaster is prevented by what occurs in the formation of pollen and embryo-sac. At this point a division of cells takes place which is called the reduction division, or, more technically, meiosis.† In it the chromosome number is reduced. The process is complex in detail but simple in principle. It can occur normally only in cells having two sets of chromosomes, or a multiple of two sets; it is impossible in haploid cells. The effect of meiosis is to sort out the two sets of chromosomes in the nucleus of the parent cell into two single sets, one set going into each daughter cell. A diploid cell may divide by mitosis, and the daughter cells also will be diploid; the like is true of a haploid cell; but a diploid

---

* From Greek words meaning, respectively, "double" and "single."

† From a Greek word meaning "less," since the number of chromosomes in a cell is thereby lessened.

Meiosis is really a special kind of mitosis; so that it is not strictly accurate to contrast the two. However it is convenient to speak of mitosis as if it did not include meiosis and so to avoid having to call it "equational mitosis" all the time.

cell may divide instead by meiosis, forming daughter cells which are haploid.

In detail, as I have said, meiosis is complex. Ordinarily in a diploid cell in a root or stem or leaf, the two sets of chromosomes seem to be hopelessly mixed: no one chromosome has any particular relation to the corresponding chromosome of the other set—its twin; the two sets are jumbled together, as one may mix two decks of cards. But when meiosis begins, the chromosomes actually become arranged in pairs; some attraction seems to draw each to its mate, and they come to lie closely side by side, every gene on one of them next to its opposite number on the other; much as if one ace of hearts in the two mixed decks could seek out the other ace of hearts, one six of diamonds the other six of diamonds, and so on, forming 52 pairs. The process of division separates the two members of each pair of chromosomes in an orderly way, so that one goes to each daughter cell; the cells formed are haploid. The actual movement of the chromosomes is far more complex than this would suggest; and four cells are formed instead of two; but the above simplified statement will suffice to make the result plain.

This is what happens in the formation of the pollen. It occurs also in the formation of the embryo-sac. Subsequent divisions in pollen and embryo-sac are mitotic; they maintain the chromosome number, the haploid number, of the cells formed by meiosis. The gametes which finally result from each history are likewise haploid. So the cycle is complete; meiosis occurs at one point in the story: in flowering plants only in the production of pollen and embryo-sac. All the other divisions of cells in the plant are mitotic. Meiosis reduces the number of chromosomes from two sets per cell to one; mitosis forms new cells with the same number of chromosomes in each as that of the parent, whatever that number was. Meiosis brings about the change from a succession of diploid cells to a succession of haploid cells. The reverse change, from haploid to diploid, occurs when the gametes unite, at syngamy.

What has all this to do with heredity, with genes? How is the history of the genes affected by this scrambling and unscrambling of sets of chromosomes?

Let us suppose that on a certain spot in a certain chromosome a gene is situated which causes (other things being equal) the development of red color in the flowers. We cannot see this gene; but by experimental evidence we know it is there; and for convenience we can give it a name, a label: R. Let us suppose further that we have a true-breeding kind of flower which regularly pollinates itself; probably the two sets of chromosomes in each of its cells will be alike in all respects, identical, so that not only will the one chromosome have a gene R at a certain spot, but the corresponding chromosome of the other set will have a twin gene R at the corresponding spot. We may label such a plant RR.

Now what happens when meiosis and syngamy occur? Obviously nothing that will produce any different effect from a succession of ordinary cell divisions. For the two R's on their respective chromosomes are sorted out into different pollen grains, into different embryo-sacs, each cell now containing only one of them; and are brought together into the new zygote again, so that the last state is exactly like the first. Inheritance through the flowers of such a race of plants, pure-breeding and self-pollinating, is exactly like inheritance in vegetative reproduction: a succession of identical individuals (providing the environment is always the same).

But if a plant is obtained by cross-pollinating unlike plants, by placing on the stigma of a red flower pollen from a variety with, say, white flowers, then the two sets of chromosomes in the zygote will *not* be identical. One will have R; the other, in the corresponding spot of the corresponding chromosome, will lack R and have instead a gene which we will call W. This will be true of every diploid cell formed by mitosis as the plant grows; we may label such a plant RW. What will the flowers of such a plant be? Red or white or pink or mottled or what?

The actual result is curious: under most conditions and in most species the flowers will be of one or the other color just as if they belonged to one of the pure-breeding races represented by the parents. Perhaps they will be red, exactly like those of the red-flowered race, just as if they had been formed as a result of self-pollination of a red flower. Just which color will predominate in such a "cross" must be determined by experiment; it cannot be predicted. Once it has been determined, it may be expected as often as you make that cross, provided conditions do not greatly vary. If the gene R turns out to be dominant over W (that is to say, if W is recessive to R), they will be related in that way in all future experiments, but not absolutely so (genes are known which are dominant at high temperatures, recessive at low temperatures). There are also genes which "blend" in expressing themselves; for example, if R and W were such genes, the flowers formed in the cross would be pink.

Now notice what meiosis and syngamy will do to a pair of mixed genes. If one chromosome carries R and its twin carries W, at meiosis these will be sorted out into different daughter cells; half the pollen grains will get R, the other half W; and the same is true of the embryo-sacs. This is true also of the gametes descended from pollen and embryo-sac; half the male gametes will have R, the other half W, and so also of the female gametes. No gamete will have both R and W, since they are all haploid; they have only single sets of chromosomes and genes.

If a flower of such a hybrid is self-pollinated, which male gametes will unite with which female gametes? Will the R male gametes seek out R female gametes? We have no reason to think so, and there seems to be no mechanism which would direct them in such a way, or into any other particular combination. Instead, it seems to be purely a matter of chance. Any one male gamete may unite with either kind of female gamete; and since there are equal numbers of the latter, there should be an equal chance of either combination. The different combinations which can be obtained are shown in the table below; any of them has the same chance of being formed as any of the rest, and so in a sufficient number of zygotes all should be represented in equal numbers.

male gamete			female gamete			zygote
R	may join with		R	to form		RR
R	may join with		W	to form		RW
W	may join with		R	to form		WR
W	may join with		W	to form		WW

But even if all these combinations actually occur and the zygotes which contain them grow into mature plants which bear flowers, there will be only two kinds, because of dominance and recessiveness. The first three combinations all lead to flowers of the same color. If all four combinations have been formed in equal numbers, as theory suggests, three-fourths of the resulting plants will have red flowers, one-fourth will have white flowers. Of course if only a few plants are grown, it is impossible to predict which combination of genes they will have, just as it is impossible to predict how two coins will fall (two heads, two tails, or one of each) if you only throw them once or twice. Our predictions are concerned only with probabilities; that is, with what is likely to happen in a large number of plants.*

Abundant experiments have confirmed these predictions. Such results were actually obtained by Gregor Mendel in the garden of the monastery at Brno, in Czecho-Slovakia, and published in a local scholarly magazine in 1866. Mendel knew nothing about chromosomes or genes, little indeed about cells; but from his breeding of peas he concluded that some "unit characters" (as he called the genes) had to behave in such a way as we now know that the chromosomes behave. A remarkable example of scientific insight!

As soon as the principles of breeding, of inheritance, outlined above are mastered, most of our questions are answered, at least partly. How does it happen that a trait appears which resembles that of a distant ancestor rather than that of the immediate parents? This is easy when we know of dominance. As we have seen, the result of crossing a pure red-flowered with a pure white-flowered

---

* If these results are difficult to visualize, obtain some red and white counters—poker chips will do; place them in two bowls, red and white in equal numbers in each bowl; and draw (without looking) one from each bowl to make a pair. Naturally you cannot predict what any one draw will give you; count the results of a number of such draws and calculate the proportion of pairs composed of two white chips.

The use of various instruments of games of chance in illustrating the mechanism of heredity does not reflect a preoccupation of the author. It merely emphasizes that a large element of chance enters into the behavior of the units concerned with the development of the characteristics of successive generations of living things.

race will be a progeny of red-flowered plants. In the offspring of the latter there is one chance in four of the appearance of a white-flowered plant like one of the "grandparents." If only a few plants are grown, there may well be none with white flowers even in this second generation; but there will be a chance of their appearance in the next generation, and so on; as long as plants of mixed inheritance are used as parents. This is one explanation of what used to be the mystery of "atavism" (inheritance from an ancestor).

Notice also that if one is looking for white-flowered plants, and if this color is due to a recessive gene, one may select those that appear and immediately have a true-breeding race (WW). But if red flowers are sought, and one selects them for propagation, there is a good chance that one will get a few white plants in the progeny; to obtain a true-breeding race is a bit more difficult (though by no means impossible).

Only the very simplest of the results of genetic experiments have been outlined above. Plants may differ—indeed they usually differ—in more than one character and in more than one gene. When such plants are crossed, the same principles apply but the results are more complicated. We can still predict the proportions of various classes of offspring but there are more classes. For instance, if pea plants which form wrinkled yellow peas are crossed with those which form smooth green peas, the first genera-tion will have wrinkled yellow seeds; in *their* progeny there will be approximately three-sixteenths with wrinkled green peas— provided a large number is grown. The chance of getting a plant like the "smooth green" parent is only one in sixteen. It is easy to see why a neighbor, having invested in hybrid corn seed and grown a fine crop from it, was disappointed when he raised a second generation from his own plants (thinking to save the expense of buying more seed). The plants of the first generation, obtained by crossing two pure inbred lines, were all alike; the second generation, which he grew from his own seed, included many of the possible combinations of the numerous genes which differed in the two lines. Comparatively few had the vigor and other desirable traits of the first hybrids.

When we come to such plants as roses and apples, which have been cultivated for hundreds, even thousands of years, we are dealing with cells in which vast mixtures of genes exist, besides numbers of extra chromosomes. In one cell there may be dozens of pairs of unlike genes. In such a case, if meiosis and syngamy occur normally, it is still possible to predict how many types of offspring are possible, and the relative chances of the different types; but it becomes merely an exercise in mathematics. The chances of getting any particular type, such as one that resembles the parent, may be only one in a million or more! Small wonder that the plant grower does not plant the seeds of Mackintosh apples or Christopher Stone roses unless he is deliberately searching for new varieties. When he wants only to carry on the original strain, he uses such methods as grafting and budding—methods of vegetative propagation. Perhaps without knowing it, he is relying on mitosis to the exclusion of meiosis in the production of new plants.

On the other hand the plant breeder deliberately takes advantage of the jumbling of many genes to find new varieties, perhaps more beautiful or more productive than the old ones. He cannot tell what he is going to get (though long experience may suggest some of the more likely combinations); he grows large numbers of plants and selects with a practised eye. This is the secret of men like Luther Burbank, the "plant wizard." They cannot (as has sometimes been asserted) direct the course of variation; but they can assist it, preside over it as it were; and use their ability as gardeners to choose and maintain what will be of value. They use, again perhaps without knowing it, both meiosis and mitosis to enrich our horticulture and agriculture.

9

✦✦✦✦✦✦

Some Other Plants

MOSTLY ABOUT FERNS

In some shady nook in the garden perhaps you grow a few ferns. In any case you have seen them in moist woods, some kinds upholstering the ledges and boulders, others filling the ravines with their tall fronds or making solid mounds of fibrous roots in swampy ground. To the farmer they are merely curiosities; they furnish no harvest. But to the gardener they have a grace and charm of their own. And to the botanist they have a special interest.

What are ferns? You have seen their tall tapering fronds, usually cut and cut again into many small segments; all growing from the ground. These are the leaves: each frond is a leaf. The stem is short, rarely seen, at or beneath the surface of the ground, often covered with scales. Many fine wiry roots also grow from the stem.

Not all ferns answer this description. Some, such as the walking fern mentioned on page 128, have small undivided leaves. Bracken has a very large three-branched leaf which arises from a slender rhizome buried deep in the soil; this grows and branches at one end, dies at the other, so gradually multiplying its kind (see p. 126). Then there are the tree ferns of the tropics, resembling palms; their stems upright, perhaps 50 feet high, crowned with spreading fronds six feet long or more. One characteristic of the leaves will always give a fern away. Most persons know the uncoiling fiddle-heads of spring, some of which can be eaten like asparagus. The same sort of growth is seen even in the tree ferns: the young leaves are coiled at the tip.

It is in the tropics and subtropics that ferns flourish best; most of them need abundant moisture and equable temperatures. In mild air dampened by ocean breezes or mountain mists multitudes of ferns cling to the limbs of trees and to shady ledges of rock. Some of these are the delicate filmy ferns, with leaves only one cell thick and unprotected against the loss of water by evaporation. The leaves of most ferns have little cutin; their blades are thin, the air spaces within relatively large; transpiration is consequently rapid in dry air. These are some of the reasons that ferns are mostly limited to moist regions. There are even ferns that grow in mud or float on water—small plants of the most unfernlike appearance. A few kinds, however, have small leathery or woolly leaves which can endure the northern climates on exposed ledges and cliffs.

Once upon a time—several hundreds of millions of years ago—there were no flowering plants, and much of the vegetation was composed of ferns. Some of these ferns formed seeds, at the tips or margins of their fronds. The extinct seed-ferns have probably left descendants, for it is generally thought that the ancestors of the flowering plants were of this group. Other, seedless, races of ferns continue to this day little changed from those distant ancestors, though perhaps in diminished numbers.

Many strange things are related of fern seed, of its magic powers and the difficulty of obtaining it; but the difficulty is so great that the powers cannot be tested. For fern seed is a myth, as far as modern ferns are concerned. Ferns form spores instead.*

If you examine the backs—the under sides—of fern fronds, you may find on some of them curious little spots, usually brown; sometimes mistaken for scale insects or other parasites. Each of these is a sorus.† They are of various shapes, sizes, and dispositions. Study with a magnifier will show that a sorus is composed of a number of minute golden or brown spheres attached by slender stalks to the surface of the leaf. Polypody has round orange sori. The sori of the lady fern are narrow, and each is covered by a

---

* The word "spore" comes from a Greek word which means "seed"; but has come to have an entirely different meaning in botany. Spores occur in many groups of plants besides ferns, and are of great importance both to plants and to us.

† From the Greek word meaning "heap."

scale which is attached along one edge to the surface of the leaf so as to form a sort of lean-to shelter. In the bladder fern the sorus is entirely enclosed in a thin membrane, which splits into several pointed scales and so exposes the parts within. Other ferns have the sorus covered by a round scale supported near one edge by a stalk—something like a lopsided umbrella. In bracken and maidenhair, and also in the filmy ferns, the sori are at the margins of the leaves, more or less covered by a flap, or enclosed in cup-shaped membranes. The under side of some leaflets of the Christmas fern is apparently covered with one large sorus; there is no division of the reproductive parts into separate small areas. The interrupted fern and the royal fern have parts of their leaves entirely devoted to reproduction and lacking any green blades; the cinnamon fern has entire leaves of this kind, mixed with the ordinary green leaves which bear no sori. Still other types of sori

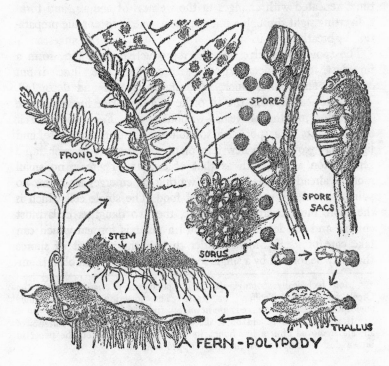

A FERN - POLYPODY

are found among ferns; it is largely by them that the ferns are classified.

The small globular objects which compose each sorus are sacs containing spores, spore-sacs.* These are the actual reproductive organs of the fern leaf. The individual spore-sac is a beautiful thing. It is a delicate hollow sphere of shallow cells with wavy outlines, usually borne up on a slender stalk. In most common species a ridge of cells with curiously thickened and orange-colored walls runs three-fourths of the way around the spore-sac, something like the crest on an ancient Greek helmet. These cells contract when they dry so as to straighten the whole crest and even turn it inside out; tearing apart the walls of the spore-sac as they do so and spilling the contents; then often snapping back again, throwing any remaining spores within the walls to some distance and closing the empty sac. The coiling and uncoiling may be many times repeated with changes in the wetness of the air, and form a diverting sight through a microscope as one moistens the preparation by breathing on it.

The spores themselves are the reproductive cells; they form a fine dust, to be understood only with a microscope.† *Each is but one cell*. The wall is thick, variously sculptured and decorated. The spores can float in the air or lie in a dry place for some time —even for months or years—without dying. Each spore, if it finally alights in a spot with suitable moisture, temperature, and light, may grow into a new fern plant. But there is no such rapid germination and growth as that of a bean. There is no small root-tip already formed within, waiting to emerge; no stem, no pair of leaves; no great reserves of food. The single cell which is the spore must enlarge and divide, the two daughter cells must enlarge and divide, and so on until a plant is formed which can take care of itself. Small wonder that of the millions of spores that may be formed by a single fern leaf most fail to establish them-

---

* More technically sporangia (singular, sporangium); *angium* is from the Greek for "vessel," "coffer," or "case." The flowering plants are called angiosperms because their seeds are in *angia*—fruits.

† If a fern frond is laid on a sheet of paper, shielded from currents of air, and removed after a few hours, its outline may remain on the paper in brown dust—the spores which have dropped from it.

selves as new, growing plants. The few that find a spot suitable for germination must emerge from their protective walls and expose their delicate growing cells, clad only in the thinnest of cellulose, to an uncertain environment.

Fern spores may be easily germinated and grown on moist paper or floating on a nutrient solution in a suitable vessel. And now comes a surprise. The plant formed by a spore may continue for many months to undergo cell divisions, to grow slowly larger, to make food in its chloroplasts, to respire; but it rarely forms a leaf, a frond; or a stem; or a root. However long it lives, it seldom resembles its parent. It is a small flat plant, sometimes heart-shaped or butterfly-shaped; if it grows in a cave or under a ledge it may stand on one edge, facing the light. Certain colorless root-hair-like cells anchor it to the earth or rock. It never gets to be more than an inch or so in size—and this is exceptionally large.

It can reproduce, this small plant, this thallus.* The reproductive organs grow on the lower side, next to the moist substratum, often projecting into a film of water. They are not spore-sacs; they form gametes instead. There are two kinds, one forming male gametes, the other female. The minute male gametes are released in large numbers from their containers (called antheridia); each is shaped something like a corkscrew, and swims actively about in water by lashing the long hairs which grow from one end.† Some of them enter the curious bottle-shaped organ in which the female gamete is contained, called the archegonium.‡ They pass through the neck of the bottle, and one unites with the large

---

* From a Greek word meaning literally a "young shoot"; it is now used for any plant, such as a seaweed, which has no proper vascular tissue, no leaves, stems, or roots such as have been described in this book. The thallus of a fern is called the prothallus or prothallium, since it comes before (*pro-*) the familiar fern plant, the plant with leaves, stem, and roots (like the hen with the egg, however, it *also* follows this plant).

† They have the astonishing name of "antherozoids"; derived from Greek words meaning "flowery" and "animal-like"; make of that what you can.

‡ *Arche-* (the "ch" is pronounced like "k" in botanical words of Greek derivation, as in "architect") is from a word meaning "to begin" and conveys the idea of being primitive or original; "gonium" is derived from the word for "offspring" or "race"; so "archegonium" designates the "original breeder" or something like that. It is found not only in ferns but in even more ancient tribes of plants; also in mosses and pines and some others.

female gamete in the basal part; thus the zygote is formed—in an archegonium instead of an embryo-sac.

This new cell, the product of syngamy, grows into a new plant; and *this* plant will not disappoint us. It forms roots, a stem, leaves —the first leaves small, unfernlike, the later ones successively larger and larger until the familiar fronds appear. Here is our fern again. Two generations instead of one are needed to complete the cycle. For the thallus is not merely a juvenile stage in the development of a fern; *it is a plant itself*. It does not grow into a leafy plant: it forms one by reproduction. We are faced by the surprising fact that a given species of fern exists in two forms, one regularly the parent of the other.

Ordinarily one propagates ferns by pieces of the stem or leaves (as already noted). This is also the common mode in nature. For the germination of spores, the growth of the thallus, the union of gametes—all these steps in the cycle require somewhat unusual conditions of moisture and temperature, or the attention of skilled technicians in the laboratory. But the rhizome of bracken, deep in the earth, can spread and multiply so easily as to become a nuisance, a weed.

The details of reproduction and inheritance are interesting. The thallus is normally haploid: one complete set of chromosomes may be found in every cell, no more. The gametes also are haploid, being formed by the thallus. The zygote is, as usual, diploid: it contains the two sets contributed by the two gametes. Every cell of the fern plant which grows from the zygote is formed by mitosis; all are traceable to the zygote through a series of mitoses; all are diploid. The spores, however, are formed by meiosis; each is haploid; each grows by mitosis into a haploid thallus; and so the cycle is complete. The two kinds of plants which alternate in the story—each normally giving rise to the other —are different in their chromosome number as in their external appearance and in their methods of reproduction.

The fern plant which we ordinarily know, the plant with the fronds, reproduces by forming spores; it is called for that reason a sporophyte, spore-plant. It is diploid but forms haploid spores by meiosis. The thallus which grows from a spore is haploid. It reproduces by forming gametes, and is therefore called a gamete-plant or gametophyte. The gametes are haploid, but join to form a diploid zygote, which grows into the sporophyte. This cycle is usually referred to as an example of the "alternation of generations.*

Many other plants have, in their life stories, a similar alternation of two unlike individuals. Mosses, for instance; true mosses—not Spanish moss, which is a flowering plant, nor reindeer moss, which is a lichen, nor Irish moss, which is a seaweed, nor the mosses found in aquaria, which are mostly flowering plants. True mosses have diminutive leaves on a small stem, both lacking a vascular system. Gametes are formed at the tips of the stems, in containers much like those of ferns and referred to under the same names. From the zygote in the archegonium sprouts a hairlike embryo, finally bearing a capsule at its tip from which spores are shed. *This* is the diploid "generation"; *this* is the sporophyte. The plant below, which forms the mats or cushions of moss, is haploid, a gametophyte. The two "generations" are discernible—but one, the diploid, is perched on the other, its haploid parent, and never leads an independent life.

Some of the seaweeds have a similar story; also the microscopic plants which form a green scum on quiet waters or grow attached

---

* Syngamy is considered by many botanists to take place in three steps: the union of cells; the union of their nuclei; and the pairing of the chromosomes in the nucleus thus formed. If we accept this view, then meiosis, in which the chromosomes are paired before being sorted out into haploid sets (p. 193), is the last act in syngamy, even though long postponed. The intimate association of the chromosomes at meiosis, often with an interchange of parts, bears out this view. The curious life cycle of the fern is thus a consequence of the postponement and separation of the steps in syngamy: the first two steps occur when the gametes unite, the third when spores are formed; and gametophyte and sporophyte are, in a sense, merely intervals in one sexual process.

There are exceptions (as usual) to many of the statements made in the text; plants are variable and will not always conform to the simple scheme which alone can be outlined in an elementary treatment. For example the thallus does sometimes bud off a vascular plant from its vegetative cells, without the intervention of gametes. In such a case both generations may have the same chromosome number.

to rocks at the margins of lakes and streams.* Horsetails also, and clubmosses have an "alternation of generations"; these are vascular plants like ferns. The same scheme may be used to explain the reproduction of pines and cycads; and even the flowering plants. In all groups of plants there is an alternation of diploid bodies with haploid; though in familiar plants the haploid "generation" is only the pollen and the embryo-sac.

CONES INSTEAD OF FLOWERS

Along our mountain ranges the wind sighs through the boughs of the pines and the pungent resinous smell of the carpet of dead needles fills the air beneath them. In other places fir and spruce replace the pines; hemlock and cedar and redwood and cypress and juniper clothe the slopes and the canyons and form leagues of lowland forest; they inhabit bogs also and are scattered over rocky hillsides; and they are favored for planting around our dwellings. These are the conifers; they have complex internal parts in the main like those of magnolia and oak and maple; they have peculiar needles or scales for leaves, and these may persist two years or more even in temperate and boreal lands; they have cones instead of flowers; but they form seeds organized in much the same way as those of beans and buckwheat.

Shake a pine branch in just the right week of spring, and a cloud of yellow dust will fly out, composed of millions of pollen grains, in structure and function essentially like those of magnolia or lily or rose or ragweed. They come from certain cones which grow in clusters at the ends of branches. A cone is something like the elongated flower of magnolia or mouse-ear, without the perianth. What corresponds to a stamen in the cones which give off the pollen is a sort of scale, tapering to the point by which it is attached to the central axis or receptacle. On its lower side are two pollen sacs, which split open to release the innumerable grains in their sulphurous cloud. Many of these stamens are

* These aquatic, flowerless plants are generally known as the algae. They constitute a number of groups of great complexity, and are not further treated in this book.

crowded spirally on the axis of the cone, which contains nothing else. Several cones grow in each cluster at the end of a branch. There are many coniferous branches on a tree. And countless trees form the forest. The numbers of pollen grains cannot be expressed in ordinary figures. They are not carried by animal visitors but float on the wind; their arrival in the only place where they can be of use to the species is a matter of chance; most are wasted; they float over the land and out to sea hundreds of miles from their native places. As they settle gradually to earth, they may get buried in the accumulated litter of dead vegetation, may be preserved under layers of moss which become peat, may finally be dug up and studied by botanists after hundreds or thousands of years of fossilized existence. So in old bogs in which fragments of ancient plants are preserved in something like their living state (as far as structure goes) we can read the history of vegetation of past ages. We can, perhaps, identify pollen which tells us that a forest of

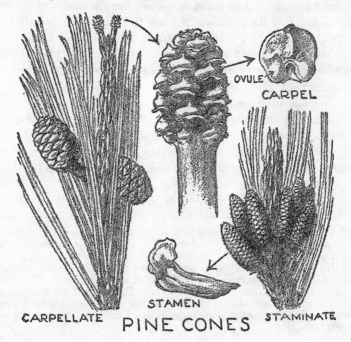

CARPELLATE   STAMEN   STAMINATE

PINE CONES

OVULE   CARPEL

pine once grew where none grows today, and that the climate of that place must have been in former times the sort of climate in which pines flourish.

All this pollen was wasted on the breeze; it did not contribute to the reproduction of the species. What became of the more fortunate grains? Where were they received? How did they function?

On other branches of the pines you can find, at the time the pollen is being shed, cones of another kind. They are rather smaller, and stand erect, singly or in pairs, at the tips of their branches. They also consist of scales arranged spirally on a central axis; all the scales stand well out and separate. Some of the pollen which fills the air everywhere will sift down between these scales and come to rest at their bases.

On the upper sides of the scales near their base are minute white swellings, two to a scale; you need a magnifier to see them. These are ovules, future seeds, essentially like the ovules of flowering plants; and the scale which bears them is generally called a carpel.* Here is the principal difference between cone and flower: the ovules of conifers are borne on the surface of their carpel; those of flowering plants are in a cavity formed by the folding of the carpel.†

The ovule of a pine has the same parts as that of a flower: a central part surrounded by an integument (which at first does not cover its apex). Instead of the embryo-sac we find a massive egg-shaped lump of cells within, having at one end several cavities reminiscent of the bottle-shaped archegonia of a fern, and like them each containing one large female gamete.

Pollen is deposited directly on or in the ovule; not on a stigma

---

* According to the morphologists it is probably a much more complex structure, reduced in the course of evolution; not strictly comparable to a carpel of a flowering plant.

† The seeds into which the ovules develop are similarly situated; whence the old terms gymnosperms ("naked seeds") and angiosperms ("covered seeds"). The latter term is still used for the flowering plants; the former has been applied not only to the conifers but to a miscellaneous lot of unrelated groups, so that it is no longer of much use in the classification of plants.

high above. The pollen-tube need grow only the short distance from the outside of the ovule, just within the integument (which closes over it) to the archegonium within. There it bursts, freeing the male gametes, one of which unites with the female gamete. The zygote is formed.

The zygote grows into an embryo, which penetrates that ovoid lump of cells already noticed. The embryo has much the same parts as that of a castor-oil bean or a buckwheat grain; but it has more than two cotyledons, a variable number. Eventually the integument becomes a hard seed-coat around the embryo and its nourishing surrounding tissue.

So we have a pine seed—an embryo lying within a nutritive tissue, both surrounded by a seed-coat. Small wonder that the nutritive tissue came to be called endosperm. But *this* endosperm has an entirely different origin from that in a lily or magnolia seed. It was there *before* syngamy, even before pollination; it was not formed as a result of the union of three nuclei at the time of syngamy.

While the seed develops, the cone also grows. That of a pine becomes much larger, the scales thicken and grow together; finally, after a year or two, the scales spread apart again, and release the seeds, now fully developed, which are attached to their surfaces. The familiar cones may remain attached to the branches for years. Other conifers, such as the arbor vitae of our foundation plantings, have small and rather fleshy cones of few scales. The cones of junipers become the "berries"; the scales become succulent and so merged together that all likeness of a cone disappears. The yews, finally, are "conifers without cones." Their ovules are borne singly, each surrounded by a collar of succulent tissue which grows up around them and forms the red "berry."

10

Spraying and Dusting

POISON IN THE GARDEN

One of the strangest things we have learned to do in our fields and gardens—a practice quite unknown to our ancestors—is to apply sundry poisonous, even disfiguring and malodorous materials to the leaves and stems of the plants on which we have bestowed all our care. Once a week, more or less, during the summer I mix with water a dirty black powder which smells rather like a skunk, place the mixture in an ingeniously contrived metal cylinder, and spray it in a fine mist over the leaves of my roses. At other times I cover them with a dust of sulphur, colored green so as to be less noticeable, but not deodorized. I also use, at frequent intervals, some dark brown stuff called Black-Leaf 40, which makes the rose garden smell like a smoking-car on the slow train through Arkansas (or elsewhere). My potatoes and sometimes my tomatoes are sprayed with a solution containing blue vitriol and lime; this goes on the iris, too. Lead arsenate is applied to the leaves of the trees. And so it goes, through a whole calendar of sprays and dusts.

These things are my weapons against the diseases and pests which afflict my garden; no gardener, no farmer can do without them any more. Plants, like men, like the other animals, suffer from diseases; a large variety of diseases, due to a large variety of causes.

210

Some of their ailments, like some of our headaches and intestinal maladies, are caused by nutritive disorders. A complete *lack* of chlorine in the soil may cause tomato leaves to wilt, turn yellow, and die from their tips downward. The *presence* of more than a very minute amount of chlorine in the air may cause a similar disease of the leaves of pineapples. The leaves of begonias in the dry air of overheated apartments may become spotted or blotched with brown and finally fall. When we know the exact causes of such diseases, we also know the remedies. If the plants have not been too severely injured they may be cured by supplying the nutritional deficiency or attending to the light, temperature, humidity, or other things in their surroundings.

Other diseases of plants, like pneumonia and tuberculosis in man, are caused by germs, by parasitic living things which invade their tissues, draw nourishment from them, exude poisons into them. Unlike most diseases of man, once the plant is diseased it cannot usually be cured.* It is for this reason we resort to sprays and dusts and (under glass) to fumigants. We have learned how to *prevent* diseases, or many of them, and how to check their progress in a plant, even if we cannot cure them.

SPOTS ON THE ROSE LEAVES

If I neglect the routine of spraying my roses, I soon find that certain leaves are marred by black spots. The margins of the spots are delicately fringed; around them are regions colored brown instead of green, passing into a yellow zone. The spots grow and spread, soon covering large areas of the leaves; all the part which is not actually black or brown may turn yellow. Finally the leaf drops; in extreme cases nothing remains of the rosebushes but leafless stalks. It is needless to add that such plants will make little food, will soon use up their reserves; and after a few such seasons must usually be replaced by fresh stock.

The diseased spots on the leaves are traced to the presence, just

* Unless the new antibiotics provide a means for a cure, which seems rather doubtful. Though such substances may rise in the sap, plants unfortunately have no circulatory system to carry therapeutic agents throughout their bodies in a short time.

beneath the layer of cutin and just above the cells of the epidermis, of long threads, living threads, formed of cylindrical cells joined end to end and encased in dark-colored walls. The threads branch and the branches lie side by side in thick strands, strands that radiate out in all directions, growing at their tips and invading fresh areas of epidermis. Some of the threads pass down between the epidermal cells and grow between them and the palisade layer; some reach more deeply into the interior of the leaf.

These threads, which are visible only with a microscope, are the body of a fungus. What is a fungus? It is a plant, a living plant; at least it is alive and it is not an animal; but it is so different in

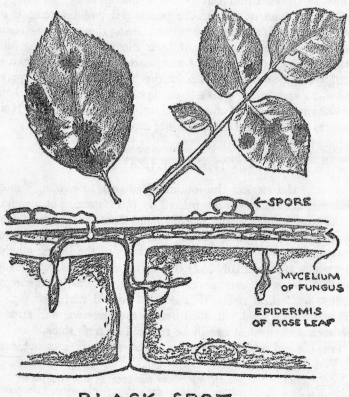

←SPORE

MYCELIUM
OF FUNGUS

EPIDERMIS
OF ROSE LEAF

BLACK SPOT

its form and in its behavior from other kinds of plants that some botanists have created a third realm of nature for it, dividing the living world into animals, plants,—and fungi.

Not all fungi are parasites upon other plants. The molds which appear on bread and cheese and leather and many other things are fungi; their bodies too are composed of branching threads, forming a delicate fur over the surface. This fungus of the black spots is also a sort of mold, its body concealed within the tissues of a leaf instead of growing freely in the air.

The cells of the fungus are in the main like those of the leaf; each is composed of a nucleus and cytoplasm surrounded by a wall; but *none of them has any chlorophyll.* The fungus cannot make any food for itself out of inorganic materials only; it must have some organic substance to feed on. The cells elongate, divide and redivide in much the same way as the cells of a flowering plant do; but little or no differentiation occurs; the cells and the strands which they compose are all much alike; they form no roots or stems or leaves or anything corresponding to such parts; no special water-conveying or food-carrying cells; there are, as we shall see, special reproductive cells.

Students of the fungi, faced with the peculiar sort of plant body briefly described above, coined their own words to name its parts. The threads of a fungus are hyphae; the entire web which makes up one fungus is a mycelium.* Almost all fungi, all but the most minute, are made of hyphae which compose a mycelium.

Here and there the threads of the creeping death within the rose leaf, the hyphae, may be seen to have delicate branches which extend directly into the living cells of the leaf. The invaded protoplasm forms a sort of gelatinous collar around the sucker that is pushed into it; but to no avail; the fungus gradually draws the life out of the cell.

In certain places the fungus mat, the mycelium, thickens up beneath the cutin and sends up many small erect branches. Each

---

* The derivation of these words from the Greek unfortunately does not help in the understanding of their application; for "hypha" is from a word meaning "web" and might better refer to the entire growth; and "mycelium" is from the word for mushroom—not very obviously comparable to a mold though, as will be seen, fundamentally like it in structure.

of these forms at its end a two-celled body with a rather thick wall: a spore.* This active growth, this formation of reproductive bodies, finally splits the cutin, and the mass of many spores is exposed to the air; the living contamination drifts out in all directions, wherever the breeze may carry it.

A spore alighting by chance on the moist surface of a leaf germinates there, sending out a small and delicate tube, a first hypha. Here is the vulnerable spot in the life of the fungus: that frail thread must live on the surface for a few hours, exposed to all the hazards of the outer world. If we have covered the leaves with a poison, if this poison still adheres to the surface in any quantity, the emerging hypha will quickly succumb; there will be no infection. It is necessary to keep the leaf protected at all times; for spores are produced by the hundreds of thousands and may drift, still living, for many miles. Most fall by the way; but if only a few come through, even only one—your rose garden is in danger.

If the spore germinates without hindrance, its growing hypha forms a sort of pad which somehow fastens itself to the waxy surface of the leaf; and from this pad sends a new hypha boring straight down through the cutin. Once it is through it has nothing more to fear; a corky wall cuts off the portion within from the remnant left above; the growing tip is now sheltered by the same cutin which protects the cells of its victim, its host; it can quickly grow into a mycelium like that which formed the spore, sending its radiating hyphae out from the center of infection, forming a new fringed black spot. Nothing can now destroy the fungus without also killing the leaf cells over and among which it is growing; at least nothing yet revealed to science.

Infected leaves which fall to the ground still contain the living fungus, and this may form a thick mass, a compact mycelium, which lives, dormant, through the winter in the dead leaf and with the return of moist and warm weather forms a new crop of infective spores. So in the spring of the year the new leaves of the roses may become diseased. The only known cure is prevention. Cover the canes with spray or dust while everything is still dormant, and keep the leaves protected in the same way during the growing

---

* For an explanation of spores see p. 200.

season. Prevent the infection by killing the hyphae as they emerge from the spores; and you can grow roses without black spots.*

FUNGI AND HISTORY

This business of spraying and dusting is more important than the saving of your rose garden—desirable as that may be. Man depends for his existence on his crops—and scarcely a crop is immune from disease. Indeed it seems as if the more a species is valued and grown, the more diseases it is afflicted by. Where do they all come from? It has been reported that in South America when new areas are opened to the cultivation of wheat, new races of the wheat rust fungus appear to which the varieties of wheat chosen for planting are not resistant—though they were chosen for their resistance to existing strains of rust. Some fungi, such as that which causes the blight which destroyed the chestnut trees of the eastern United States, were relatively innocuous in their original homes, but fatal when introduced into a new environment.

The year 1846 was a terrible year in many parts of Europe; particularly in the poorer parts. In the preceding year the potato plants had been stricken with a mysterious and fatal murrain, a terrible affliction which blackened the foliage and even rotted the tubers in the ground; in wet weather it could run through entire fields in a few days. Even apparently sound tubers rotted after they were harvested and stored. Suffering was dire in many parts of Europe; but in Ireland the poor tenant farmers, with no reserves of food or money, faced starvation; potatoes were the staff of life. During the winter of 1845-46 and throughout the ensuing year, hundreds of thousands labored on public works, the only form of "relief" which the government could conceive; something like eight million pounds were spent in such works; yet many did die of starvation and the attendant typhoid. No remedy could be found for the blight; it had come to stay. In the following fifteen years,

---

* It is not my purpose here to give specific directions for the control of particular plant diseases. The appropriate poisons are sold under many proprietary names; and there are excellent books which instruct in their use. It is our business here to elucidate the principles upon which the control of disease depends. Control has a background of pure botany.

a million people died in that small country as a direct result of this plant disease; and a million and a half emigrated. The latter came mostly to America, where, in the rapid growth of the country, they could find work with pick and shovel for enough money to furnish their modest wants. The history of the United States and its national character would have been different without this tide of cheap laborers and their descendants; yet few historians accord a place in their writings to the parasitic fungus which was the cause of it all.

The late blight of potatoes (which may affect tomatoes also under certain climatic conditions) is caused by spores which send hyphae into the leaves and form a mycelium within.* The mycelium grows rapidly in the spaces between the cells, pushing suckers into them and exuding a poison which kills and blackens the tissues around it; and sends out meanwhile numerous branches through the stomata, branches which form more spores: spores by the thousands, to infect new plants. As with the rose disease, the spore must germinate on a moist surface; its first hypha must creep over that surface until it makes or finds an opening to the interior (they sometimes enter through the stomata). In this stage it is easily killed; periodic application of the old standard spray called Bordeaux mixture will prevent infection and save the crop. But before this was discovered—and it was years before some one stumbled onto it—there was terrible suffering among the poor growers of potatoes.

It was hard, indeed, to convince even the learned that the cause of the disease was a parasite, a fungus. John Lindley, one of the most eminent of English botanists of that time, said that it was due to the weather (and indeed such diseases spread more rapidly in wet weather, when the spores can more easily find moist surfaces on which to germinate; the spores of the blight fungus germinate best in cool wet weather). The Reverend Miles Joseph Berkeley and his fellow experts on fungi had as much trouble to establish the truth as Louis Pasteur did a little later to prove that animal

---

* The hyphae of this mycelium are not divided by walls into separate cells; many nuclei float in a common cytoplasm. This is a frequent type of organization among the "lower" plants.

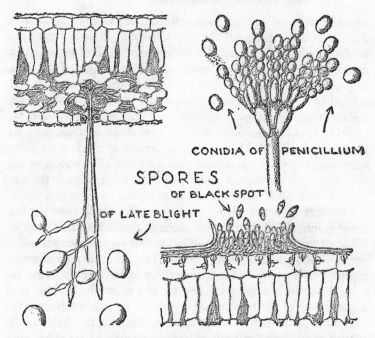

CONIDIA OF PENICILLIUM

SPORES
OF BLACK SPOT

OF LATE BLIGHT

diseases are caused by bacteria and not vice versa. And of course discovery of the remedy had to wait on knowledge of the cause. Meanwhile history ran its course.

PLANT PATHOLOGY

The diseases of plants are legion. Many have been known for a long time and some of these—not all—are successfully controlled by those who know what to do and take the necessary trouble. New diseases, of greater or less importance, are constantly being reported. Some have struck with devastating suddenness. The chestnut trees of the northeastern United States, a familiar and valuable source of food and timber only a couple of generations ago, are practically extinct; a fungus was responsible. We are currently contending with the Dutch elm disease and the oak wilt; and the outcome of these battles is as yet uncertain. Rusts and smuts of wheat and other grains cause annual losses of millions of dollars. Parasitic fungi inhabit the soil, lying in wait for tender seedlings which they cause to "damp off." There are scabs of apples and potatoes, wilts of tomatoes and asters, rots of the roots of peas and delphinium and of the wood of living trees, galls and cankers on roses and dogwoods and cedars and many other plants, leaf-spots on almost every species . . . an endless list. And, in addition to all these, other diseases caused by bacteria, such as pear blight, and still others caused by viruses, of which more later. Moreover, the plant grower must contend also with insects which suck and chew the life out of his plants; of these it is not feasible to write in a book on botany.

The rusts are some of our most serious diseases, affecting the cereal grains, the staff of life for much of the human race, besides a host of less important plants—blackberries and raspberries, hollyhocks, sunflower, carnations, violets. This multitude of diseases is caused by a swarm of fungi, each more or less limited to one or a few kinds of host plants. They are not generally fatal, as late blight is fatal to potato plants; they live almost unsuspected within the tissues of the host, stealing its food, reducing its vigor and its output; finally bursting forth in spots or streaks on the leaves and stems—the spores thus revealed being often of the reddish color which gives the disease its name. The extraordinary thing about these fungi is the number of kinds of different reproductive bodies which they form. The ordinary rust fungus of wheat boasts of no less than five kinds of spores. Furthermore, though some of these spores may infect new wheat plants, as one might expect, others are harmless to wheat and will attack only the wild barberry. Efforts have been made to exterminate barberry in the hope of denying the fungus one of its hosts, the substratum for one part of its life cycle; but there were holes in the theory (the story is too complex to be given here in detail). Other rust fungi have this curious addiction to two quite unrelated hosts. That which causes spots on apple leaves also makes galls on red cedar. The fungus of the blister rust of white pines flies also to wild currants and gooseberries. The rust fungi are difficult to control and cause serious losses in our fields and forests.

Among the most baffling of diseases are those caused by viruses. A virus (the Latin word means simply "poison") is an agent which shares properties of living and of nonliving matter; it stands in the borderland of life and death. It will pass through filters which hold back the smallest cells; yet it multiplies itself within its host. It has been crystallized, and proves to be of the nature of a protein. It is frequently transmitted by sucking insects, aphids, leafhoppers, and the like, being injected by them deep into healthy tissues. Viruses cause many different symptoms; the best known are the mosaic diseases, for example of tobacco, so called because they manifest themselves as a pattern of small light green or yellow areas among those of the normal color. The leaves may also become curled and crinkled in various ways. Aster yellows (which affects many other plants also) is caused by a virus; also curly-top of sugar-beets. Strangely enough, we grow some plants *because* they are diseased; the mottled or variegated flowers of some tulips and camellias owe their decorative peculiarities to a virus. Viruses are also known which cause human diseases; measles, influenza, poliomyelitis, rabies are examples. Prevention of virus diseases in plants is difficult. We try to avoid sources of infection; to make our gardens sanitary as we make our houses sanitary. And some progress has been made in breeding varieties of potatoes, cucumbers, beans, beets, and other crops which are more or less immune: at least resistant. Perhaps the new knowledge of antibiotics will afford protection against these plagues.

To contend with a legion of enemies we have an army of pathologists; in the Department of Agriculture of the United States, in the experiment stations of the 48 states, in the universities and colleges, in many industrial laboratories. They study the modes of reproduction of the fungi, discover the vulnerable points in their history, invent the appropriate poison to kill the parasite without damaging the host. Or they try to combine by breeding the desirable qualities of the crops with the resistance or immunity to disease which may occur in otherwise undesirable varieties, even in wild species.

The key to the control of many fungous diseases is their method of infection; as we have seen already in tracing the story of black spot and of late blight. The fungus must enter the host plant, must send out a delicate living, growing thread to find a way in; and this thread can be killed, its entrance prevented, by sprays and dusts. Hence the practical measures to be taken depend first upon botanical study of the fungi, whose structure and reproductive peculiarities may often be learned by growing them in glass vessels on synthetic foods; second upon chemical study of substances which are poisonous to emerging hyphae without causing injury to the plants they are meant to protect.

Many fungi, however, gain entrance directly into plants through wounds. The rots of tree-trunks are of this kind; about all we can do is to take care not to leave living cells or moist wood exposed to the air any more than we can help. The chestnut disease was transmitted by a beetle which burrowed beneath the bark; no way of preventing this was ever discovered. With some of the more virulent diseases measures must be taken comparable to human sanitation. A wilt of tomatoes is easily spread by the tools and even the hands of the gardener. Some diseases are seed-borne, and are controlled by dipping the dormant seeds in poisons (which kill spores on the surface without penetrating the seed-coat) or by carefully heating them to a temperature which will kill the mycelium inside without damaging the embryo. Some parasites winter in soil or in dead plant remains; this may necessitate rotation of crops or sterilization of soil, according as one is running a farm or a greenhouse.

On page 24 some account was given of the antibiotics, those substances which are formed by certain plants (mostly fungi) and prevent the growth of other plants (bacteria and fungi); penicillin being the first to be definitely known. If these substances can prevent the growth of bacteria which cause diseases of man, why can they not be the enemies also of the bacteria and fungi of plant disease? A mass of evidence, which is increasing even as I write, shows that they can. Streptomycin, for instance, can be introduced into chrysanthemums by feeding it to their roots; and they are then safe, at least for a time, from bacterial wilt. The same antibiotic is being used for pear blight with some success. Aureomycin will prevent the formation of crown gall on tomatoes and marigolds. Noformicin sprayed on bean leaves has been shown to diminish the severity of mosaic of beans. Such names as terramycin, helixin, filipin, chloramphicol are appearing more and more in the literature of plant pathology. We are evidently on the threshold of a new era in dealing with plant diseases.

THE SCAVENGERS

To end a treatment of the fungi at this point would leave an impression that all these plants are our enemies. This is very far from the truth. Indeed it would be more accurate to say that we could not get along without them; at least not without certain kinds.

To begin with, not all fungi are parasites. It is true that they all lack chlorophyll. They cannot make food for themselves out of carbon dioxide and water and other inorganic materials; they must have at least one organic substance provided for them, as a basis for their processes of manufacture. Some, as we have seen, get their organic material directly from the living cells of green plants; others enter into a similar relation with living animal cells; these are the parasites. But still others feed on organic matter which is no longer a part of living cells. They grow on and in the nonliving remains of plants, on dead leaves and dead wood. They flourish on foods which are made from plant substances—jams, jellies, preserves, bread, cake; and on things derived from animals, such as leather and cheese. All these fungi are called saprophytes. There is a third group, which enter into partnerships with other plants, a relationship apparently of mutual benefit. The commonest of these are the fungi which invade the roots of many trees, such as beeches, forming a fine web in or around the roots, and, in exchange for their food, assisting in the absorption of materials from the soil. An entire class of plants, the lichens, is formed of a union between fungi and the minute green plants called algae. Such arrangements are known as symbiotic ("living together").

If we add the bacteria to the fungi we greatly enlarge all three classes: parasites, saprophytes, and symbionts. But the bacteria, although they do lack chlorophyll like the fungi, differ from all other plants in so many ways that they form the subject of a distinct science, with its own special techniques and problems. They are not separately considered in this book, but mentioned only as they share the work of the fungi proper.

The army of saprophytes is responsible for ridding the earth of dead organic bodies. Were it not for them, we should be faced with the problem of removing, by fire or otherwise, the bodies of all the plants and animals that ever lived on earth; for their decay and reabsorption into the earth is the work of the saprophytes. Moreover, most of the nutrients of the earth would eventually be locked up in these organic bodies, and little would be left for new forests or new crops. Recall the nitrogen cycle, for instance (p. 85): the nitrates in the soil, upon which green plants depend for their nitrogen, are replenished by the breakdown of the proteins of plant and animal bodies; partly while they are alive, by their own respiration; mostly after they are dead—and this is where the sapropyhtes come in.

They break down organic to inorganic substances, materials which will dissolve into water and play their part in the nutrition of the flowering plants. This is the principle of the compost heap; it is an arrangement in which organic remains are gathered together under conditions that favor the action of saprophytes. Something has been said (page 97) of the remarkable power of these organisms to penetrate such obdurate foods as wood. Because of the substances which they form, some saprophytes are of direct use to man in his industry: for example the molds responsible for cheeses of many kinds.

These fungi are of an infinite variety, characterized not only by being black or white or gray or green* but by intricate and various types of reproduction. Most kinds form both spores and gametes—the formation of the latter constituting what is known as the "perfect stage" of the fungus. The spores of many are pinched off at the ends of hyphae, as those of the black spot fungus are; these are called conidia.† Some form chains of such spores,

---

* Many fungi are green (as in Roquefort cheese); but the pigment is not chlorophyll and has no use in the manufacture of food.

† From a Greek word meaning "dust."

the hypha again dividing at its end before the spore already formed has parted company with it. The fungus which forms penicillin is named Penicillium, from a word meaning "a brush," because of its cluster of branched chains of conidia. Other fungi form their spores within membranes, usually of a spherical or oval shape: spore-sacs. Some grow in the water, and have spores which swim by means of vibrating hairs. The sexual processes are too complex to be described here (and are of no direct concern to the grower of plants). Suffice it to say that they have some features which are different from those of all other plants. The result of sexual reproduction is frequently to provide a "resting body," a structure which can become dormant like a seed and endure for some time unhurt by drying and low temperature. Some of these are seen as minute black specks in the powdery mildew which grows on the surface of leaves of lilac, clover, roses, and many other plants. Each of these hard-shelled objects contains one or several spore-sacs of a special kind called asci (singular, ascus); these are part of the sexual process and in them meiosis occurs.

Almost all fungi form spores in incredible numbers and the spores may travel for hundreds or thousands of miles—even across the Atlantic—and still remain alive and capable of germination. It is small wonder that our ancestors, lacking a knowledge of such microscopic living things, looked upon the appearance of molds, mushrooms, and the like as a *result* of the decomposition of plant and animal remains, rather than the cause. "Spontaneous generation" was once the simplest explanation, indeed the only possible explanation, of the sudden growth of mold on food or toadstools on manure.

Mushrooms and toadstools need special consideration; for at first sight they do not seem to share the general structure of the fungi, a mycelium made of hyphae. If, however, a part of a mushroom is dissected, torn apart, and examined microscopically, it is at once evident that it is made of a great mass of interwoven threads, hyphae. A mushroom is, in fact, a mycelium compacted, as it were, into a solid form with definite surfaces, a definite shape. It is formed in a mould; though the shaping force comes, in some way, from within, instead of being imposed from without. Its

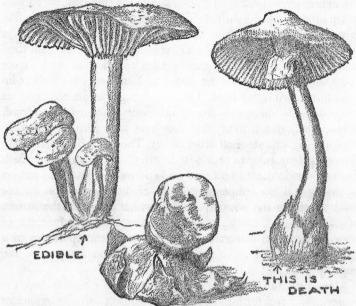

EDIBLE

THIS IS DEATH

TOADSTOOLS AND EARTH-STAR

structure is in marked contrast to that of the stems and leaves and roots of a flowering plant, with their various types of cells so geometrically arranged. Moreover, the mushroom as we see it is only a part of a plant—the reproductive part. The rest is in the substratum, the earth or leaf-mold or manure in which it is growing; and this buried part is a more typical mycelium, composed of a web of branching threads mixed with the surrounding matter. Like other fungi, the mycelium of a mushroom must have organic material; if it lives in soil, it may quickly exhaust its food and grow outwards where more is available. Mushrooms appear on the new, vigorous mycelium; hence the "fairy rings" often seen in meadows, where organic matter is present but not abundant.

The gills of the mushroom, radiating on the lower side of the cap, bear spores, neither in chains nor in sacs, but pinched off from small projections which arise (usually in fours) on a special cell called a basidium. Likewise the pores or irregular slits of a bracket fungus contain basidia. And all the internal cells of a puff-ball or earth-star become basidia and turn into a vast mass of minute spores. As in an ascus, meiosis usually occurs in basidia. Two great groups of fungi are classified and named by their possession of asci or basidia.

A word to the unwary: there is no botanical distinction between mushrooms and toadstools. To the botanist the two words are equivalent; poisonous species occur in the same families as edible ones. There is no easy way to distinguish edible from poisonous kinds; *you must know the fungi*—or consult an expert. All the traditional tests, such as the blackening of a silver spoon, are unreliable; they belong to folk-lore, not to science—and have had their victims. And the need for knowledge here is serious. Some poisonous fungi may cause you severe nausea and pain, even induce coma, but without seriously threatening your life. *Others are deadly.* Some of their poisons are not destroyed by cooking, and no antidote is known; they cause an almost inevitable and painful death. These are the enemies which render the whole race suspect and enforce the greatest caution on all of us in bringing fungi to our tables. It is safe, of course, to use the mushrooms grown for the market in cellars, abandoned mines, caves, and specially built mushroom houses. These fungi are raised from spawn—mycelium —of known parentage and salubrity.

Appendix: The
Naming of Plants

Plants were first named in various tongues: Egyptian, Chinese, Mayan, Hebrew, Greek, Latin, German, English. . . . The names of one man might be without meaning to another; as even today in the United States the names used in one state are unknown—or used for different plants—in another. Fortunately, because of the accidents of history, educated Europeans of the seventeenth and eighteenth centuries were still speaking—and writing—Latin rather than their vernaculars for scholarly pursuits. So when the herbalists described the plants they knew, they mostly used Latin. And when Ray and Tournefort and Bauhin and Linnaeus laid the foundations of modern botany, they wrote in Latin and named the plants in Latin. So our accepted names for all plants are Latin names (or at least names done into Latin form); they are intelligible to the well-informed in all countries of earth. Not only the scientist but the gardener uses them, if he wants to be sure of understanding and being understood.

From early times man knew the different kinds of plants, in a broad sense: what we now call the genera.* Maples differ from oaks in ways that are apparent; roses are easily distinguished from blackberries; violets form a group different from buttercups. The genera received distinctive names in various languages; the Romans gave the name Acer to the maples, Quercus to the oaks; Rosa and Viola are names we still know; Rubus was a bramble. Europeans of later centuries continued to use these names, and when they wanted to name plants unknown to the Romans they made up names for them from Latin

* *Genus* in Latin means "race" or "family," hence "kind." *Genera* is the plural.

226

stems. In 1542 Leonhart Fuchs of Tübingen coined the name Campanula, "little bell," for the bluebells of northern lands.

But within such genera of plants as maples or roses there are many distinct kinds, differing in less obvious ways: the species.* Naturally as botanists came to know more and more species they had more and more difficulty in specifying the differences among them. If you know only two kinds of roses, York and Lancaster, it is easy to name them Rosa alba and Rosa rubra (in English, white rose and red rose). But when you have run across 12 species, as Carl Linnaeus had by 1753, some with white flowers but most with red or pink flowers, your names, if they are still to define the differences among the species, must become more complex. So Linnaeus wrote "Rosa caule aculeato, pedunculis laevibus, calycibus semipinnatis glabris" and "Rosa caule petiolisque aculeatis, calycis foliolis indivisis" for two roses with white flowers.†

Then Linnaeus hit upon the happy device of using *one word*, with the name of the genus, to refer to the species. This word, usually an adjective (such as *alba*) only described one feature of the plant, perhaps not an important one; but, since it was used *only once in that genus* it led you straight to the more ample description by which you could recognize the species. Several roses have white flowers but only one was named *Rosa alba*.

This system, the binomial system, persists to the present day and is now indispensable in botany (and zoology). Every species is in a genus. The genus is named by a single word (*Acer, Rosa, Viola*). The species is named by two words‡ (*Acer rubrum, Rosa canina, Rubus odoratus*), of which the first is the name of the genus, the second a qualifying epithet. The epithet is usually an adjective, agreeing with the generic name in gender; but occasionally it is another noun, in the genitive (*Cornus nuttalli*) or in apposition (*Lobelia cardinalis*).

Within the species still smaller units of classification may be recognized: subspecies, varieties, forms (in that order). Each of these is named by adding another epithet; for instance, *Primula sinensis* var. *fimbriata, Cornus florida* f. *rubra*. This can result in names of great complexity—almost as bad as the old pre-Linnaean ones; into which it is not necessary to enter here. The layman should notice that "species" and "varieties" are quite different units; they are often confused in ordinary speech and popular writing.

---

* The English word is the same as the Latin from which it comes; and both singular and plural are the same.

† "Rose with prickly stem, smooth peduncles, and smooth semipinnate calyx" and "Rose with prickly stem and petioles, the leaves of the calyx undivided."

‡ Occasionally three or more, one for the genus and two or more, hyphened, for the species: Aster novae-angliae.

Genera which are more or less alike and hence probably related by descent from a common (though distant) ancestor are placed together in one family; so *Rosa* and *Rubus* are included in the rose family. The name of a family is generally formed by adding the ending -aceae to the name of one of its genera: Rosaceae, Violaceae, Aceraceae. Related families compose an order, whose name ends in -ales: Rosales, Cornales, Liliales. Orders in turn are grouped in the larger divisions of the plant kingdom, such as the Angiospermae (flowering plants), Coniferophyta (conifers), Fungi, etc. The names of these large groups are not at present formed in any prescribed way.

It has unfortunately happened that, since Linnaeus' time, different botanists have inadvertently given different names to the same plant, or used the same name for different species. Opinions have also differed on the proper classification of a plant: to one it has seemed a distinct species, to another nothing more than a variety of some other species; and so it acquires several names. After many years of confusion, botanists of many countries agreed to adopt rules of nomenclature by which such difficulties could be resolved and the correct application of names settled. These rules, several times revised, remain in force today as the *International Code of Botanical Nomenclature*. Their guiding principle is that the earliest name since 1753* has precedence over all others, providing it meets certain technical requirements. This applies even to the spelling of the name; we are not permitted to change it from the original, though we may now use a different spelling of the same word. Certain species have the epithet *pensylvanica*, and since this was a spelling current at the time they were named we are not authorized to correct it to "pennsylvanica." Latin words often differ from closely related English words; *sibirica* is the correct form for Siberian, most nurserymen and some horticulturists notwithstanding; and this also must not be changed. It is true that it is usually impossible for a plant grower who is not also a professional botanist to look up the correct name for a species or variety. When in doubt he should consult the nearest university or botanical garden.

Besides all the complexities of botanical nomenclature there are the horticultural names of varieties, the trade names, the "fancy" names, often registered in periodical publications. Some effort has been made to write a code of rules for these also; but it is almost impossible. Garden varieties, mostly of such mixed inheritance that they can be maintained only by vegetative propagation, not found in nature but innumerable in cultivation, are named usually by words in the vernacular; sometimes descriptive, sometimes fanciful, sometimes commemorative (Chrysanthemum Moonbeam, *Rosa* Else Poulsen,

* The date of publication of Linnaeus' *Species plantarum*, in which the binomial system was introduced.

Phlox paniculata Magician). Unfortunately some are referred to also by Latin epithets which resemble botanical names and may be confusing (*Viola cornuta atropurpurea*); and some growers will join the epithet of a form or variety directly to the generic name as if it were a species (*Clematis alba* instead of *Clematis lanuginosa* var. *alba*).

So long as plants vary and so long as variants are offered in the trade, so long must the gardener pick his way carefully through the jungle of trade and fancy names and hope that botanical nomenclature will remain comparatively systematic and stable.

Index [*]

---

[*] A page-number followed by the letter n refers to a footnote on that page.